WISCONSIN UNDERGROUND

A GUIDE TO CAVES, MINES, AND TUNNELS IN AND AROUND THE BADGER STATE

Other books by Doris Green

Elsie's Story: Chasing a Family Mystery

Explore Wisconsin Rivers

Minnesota Underground and the Best of the Black Hills

WISCONSIN UNDERGROUND

A GUIDE TO CAVES, MINES, AND TUNNELS IN AND AROUND THE BADGER STATE
(2ND EDITION)

DORIS GREEN

HENSCHELHAUS PUBLISHING, INC.
MILWAUKEE, WISCONSIN

The photos included in this book were taken by the author unless otherwise noted.

HenschelHAUS Publishing, Inc.
2625 S. Greeley St. Suite 201
Milwaukee, WI 53207
www.henschelHAUSbooks.com

HenschelHAUS books may be purchased for educational, business, or sales promotional use. For information, please email info@henschelHAUSbooks.com

ISBN: 978159598-645-0
E-ISBN: 978159598-650-4
LCCN: 2018948510

Publisher's Cataloging-In-Publication Data
(Prepared by The Donohue Group, Inc.)

Names: Green, Doris (Doris M.), author.
Title: Wisconsin underground : a guide to caves, mines, and tunnels in and around the Badger State / Doris Green.
Description: 2nd edition. | Milwaukee, Wisconsin : HenschelHaus Publishing, Inc., [2018] | Previously published: Black Earth, Wis. : Trails Books, ©2000.
Identifiers: ISBN 9781595986450 | ISBN 9781595986504 (ebook)
Subjects: LCSH: Caves--Wisconsin--Guidebooks. | Mines and mineral resources--Wisconsin--Guidebooks. | Tunnels--Wisconsin--Guidebooks. | LCGFT: Guidebooks.
Classification: LCC GB605.W6 G74 2018 (print) | LCC GB605.W6 (ebook) | DDC 551.44709775--dc23

Cover design by Lisa Imhoff, Grey Horse Studio
Photo: Crystal Cave, Spring Valley, Wisconsin

To Mom, Dad, and Aunt Elsie, who introduced my sister and me to the mystery and wonder of underground worlds on a family trip to the Cave of the Mounds in 1956.

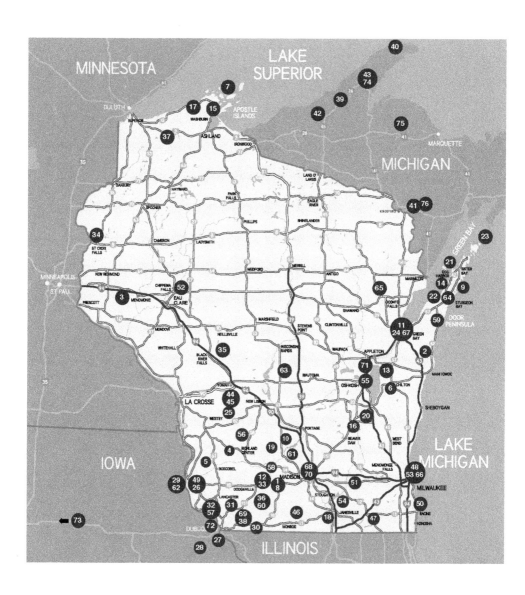

MINNESOTA

LAKE SUPERIOR

MICHIGAN

ILLINOIS

IOWA

LAKE MICHIGAN

TABLE OF CONTENTS

FOREWORD

Back in 2000, the first edition of *Wisconsin Underground* appeared, to the delight of readers and explorers. Writer and author Doris Green did an outstanding job researching the many public caves, cave related displays, mines, and other underground points of interest. She brought them all together in one easy to read book. It was an immediate success with the public, and cavers alike.

Now, eighteen years later, Green, who is a caver and member of the Wisconsin Speleological Society, has once again traveled all across the state and researched, updated, revised, and expanded her book. The result is this fascinating and improved second edition.

No matter what your interests are in publicly available underground features, manmade or otherwise, it is all covered here. From show caves to public cave features, Green has managed to bring them to the attention of the traveling public. The impressive developed show caves you can tour exist in six different Wisconsin counties. You can visit the featured undeveloped public caves on your own, and this is your guide to adventure! Taken even one step further, the book includes two manmade mines that offer guided tours, as well as a number of superb museum cave displays, and even historical signs and kiosks that educate the public on our caves and karst.

WISCONSIN SPELEOLOGICAL SOCIETY

In presenting a book such as this, one has to start somewhere. A good starting point is the non-profit Wisconsin Speleological Society. This group was formed by University of Wisconsin-Madison students in February 1960. Now, well over half a century later, the organization has grown, matured, and welcomed people from all ages and walks of life. Some do cave excavating, some are geologists, others are historians and biologists, while others like cave exploration or mapping, not to mention even cave diving! Other cavers make good cave guides, handle finances, edit caving newsletters, design signs, and all the other needed aspects of a truly functioning cave organization. Cave projects over the years have included everything from mapping both wild and developed show caves, to remote cave diving, as well as assisting and doing cave-related displays for the education of the public. Others present fascinating cave lectures to the public. To learn more, visit their web site at www.wisconsincaves.org

The Wisconsin Speleological Society is a grotto of the National Speleological Society. Over 8,500 members exist nationwide. Their web site is www.caves.org.

DISTRIBUTION OF WISCONSIN CAVES

The glaciation from 10,000 to 12,000 years ago in northern Wisconsin, resulted in glacial till from melt waters covering most of the caves that almost certainly existed. In the unglaciated southwestern Wisconsin, a remarkable array of caves and speleological points of interest still exist for anyone who loves to explore the underworld. This is called the unglaciated, or "Driftless Area." It is a remarkable karst landscape all its own.

While this book generally covers the public caves and related displays and attractions, it is worth mentioning that a total of well over 400 caves and cave-related features exist in Wisconsin. This number includes sea caves, which generally are rather small, wave-formed caves found along the Wisconsin shores of Lake Superior and Lake Michigan.

If you count caves and some sinkhole features that are recognized by the Wisconsin Speleological Society, a grand total of 616 caves and/or sinkhole features are listed. Although most are located on private property and are not accessible to the public, a few interesting observations can be made. These features are found in exactly half of Wisconsin's seventy-two counties. Nationally, some 50,000 to 70,000 caves are known to exist in the entire United States.

The majority of Wisconsin caves are located in the unglaciated counties of Southwest Wisconsin. It should be pointed out that the three leading counties with the most caves, or significant cave and sinkhole features, are: Grant County with 106, followed by Iowa County with 88, and Richland County with 69.

North Central Wisconsin and Southeast Wisconsin generally have no caves, or even cave-related features. North Central Wisconsin lacks the soluble Niagara dolomite bedrock where caves can form. In Southeast Wisconsin, tons of glacial overburden cover the bedrock and any pre-existing caves.

Although glaciers also covered Door County, many caves are still known there, since the Niagara Escarpment usually has two feet or less of topsoil over its Niagara dolomite bedrock. This rock is also known as "dolostone," and is less soluble than regular limestone due to its higher magnesium content.

Horseshoe Bay Cave, or Tecumseh Cave, (page 57) is the longest known undeveloped, or wild cave, in Wisconsin. This Door County cave has been mapped to 3,103 feet in length. Cave divers have explored a fifty-two-foot long water-filled siphon to find another 276 feet of air-filled cave continuing on! So, the mystery of how far the cave actually goes, is still unknown!

As for Northwest Wisconsin, Crystal Cave in Pierce County (page 23) is the longest known natural cave in the state. It is a multi-level show cave with about a mile of mapped cave passageways. Another nearby cave that is about 1,000 feet long, is within 200 to 300 feet of being connected to it! The lure to discover and explore beneath the rolling hills of Wisconsin is an on-going process.

MINES, TUNNELS, MUSEUMS, AND VARIOUS FEATURES

As if naturally formed show caves and wild caves are not enough, Doris Green has traveled across the state to cover a myriad of other subterranean features from man-made mines to tunnels, museum cave displays, and other buried points of interest. Not only has she meticulously covered all of Wisconsin, but she has included the nearby sites in Iowa and the Upper Peninsula of Michigan.

As the average age of the American population has increased, the number of handicapped accessible man-made mine and museum cave sites in particular has also increased. It is hard to know where to start to describe this varied kaleidoscope of features, but Green has eagerly and painstakingly sought them out no matter where they are located. As a result, this second edition of Wisconsin Underground is far more complete than her already impressive first edition. Just for example, tourist rich Door County has no fewer than eight speleological points of interest alone, from wild caves one can explore to numerous museum cave displays! Speaking of museum displays, be sure to note that not only museums with cave displays or replicas are listed, but even museums with minerals or old mining equipment, are described. And don't forget the underground mines, especially the lead and zinc mines of Southwest Wisconsin and the copper and iron mines of Michigan's Upper Peninsula. All will whet your appetite to explore both the natural and man-made attractions of the area. You might say that speleology has no bounds!

ON TO THE FUTURE!

It should be pointed out that natural caves are the Last Frontier of man. Humans have used rope and technical mountain climbing gear and climbed over 29,000 feet up Mt. Everest in Nepal. By the same token, man has used an expensive and specially designed submarine to descend some seven miles under the Pacific Ocean in the Marianna Trench off the coast of Southeast Asia. Yet anyone with rather modest means can still find virgin, or unexplored cave passages today. That is the lure of the unknown that is the driving force enjoyed both by cavers and the public alike in exploring this hidden world beneath our feet!

Keep in mind that for every known cave in a certain area, at least one unknown cave is likely to exist as well. In fact, many caves are known to have no natural entrances. Caves found in quarry operations, like Cave of the Mounds, are one primary example. So, sit back in your seat, grab your copy of this new and updated Wisconsin Underground, and explore the wide variety of cave and other subterranean features that our state has to offer. I highly recommend this book to the traveling public and cavers alike.

Gary K. Soule, Cave Archivist and Historian
Wisconsin Speleological Society
Sturgeon Bay, Wisconsin

INTRODUCTION

E ntering a silent cavern or tunnel is like picking up a good mystery: We want to know, "What lies ahead in the darkness?" Yet, there is a difference between reading a novel and journeying beneath the earth's surface. Exploring one of Wisconsin's underground spaces leads to more questions as often as to a neat, no-loose-ends conclusion. The darkness and mystery attract us today as much as they did the earliest travelers here, who wondered what they would find around the next bend in the river or beneath the next blow of the pick in an exploratory mine tunnel.

Years before statehood, lead miners rushed to the area that is now Southwest Wisconsin, following rediscoveries of lead in the region where Native Americans had once dug the mineral. The miners spent long days searching out claims and occasionally lived in the holes they had burrowed into the ground or crude huts roofed with sod—giving Wisconsin its name, the Badger State.

Ever since, Wisconsin's underground resources have provided industry and recreation, as well as a rich source of folklore and legend. The search for hidden mineral deposits and the lure of unknown cave passages have drawn many explorers to delve deep beneath the surface of the natural landscape. Who knows what one will find under the next ridge or through the passage beyond? These mysteries still draw adventurers of all ages and abilities.

WHAT'S IN THE BOOK?

This second edition provides an introduction for modern-day adventurers who want to know more about the underground Wisconsin that sustained many Native Americans, attracted the early miners, and lured the state's first European explorers. Whether you're drawn by a desire to learn more about Badgerland history or just want to experience an unordinary adventure, this book offers a starting point. Tossed into a glove box or knapsack, it can serve as a treasure map to Wisconsin's underground wonderlands.

Divided into four sections, the book is loosely organized according to the three types of sites. Section I focuses on the underground attraction that Wisconsin travelers are probably most familiar with—providing a guide to more than twenty accessible caves and rock shelters. These range from the well-known and well-developed Cave of the Mounds near Mount Horeb to the rugged and more recently opened caves at Ledge View Nature Center near Chilton. You also can find directions to intriguing sites in northeastern Iowa, including Spook Cave, which offers an underground boat tour, and Maquoketa Caves State Park, which features about a dozen caves of varying shapes and sizes.

Though less numerous, Wisconsin's mining attractions are at least as fascinating as its caves. In fact, in several cases, the state's early miners began their digs by enlarging existing caves. Section II describes two old mines you can visit and a handful of related mining sites across Wisconsin, as well as several copper and iron mines, located a manageable drive away in Michigan's Upper Peninsula.

Section III explores a variety of historic tunnels and other underground spaces dug for different purposes—beer storage, train passageways, human escape routes, and lead shot production, to name a few. All are found within Wisconsin's borders, with the single exception of a series of storage caves dug out of the bluffs across the Mississippi River in McGregor, Iowa.

In Section IV you can find descriptions of the full-size cave and mine replicas featured at various Wisconsin museums and other sites, as well as a few over the border in Iowa and Upper Michigan. They can deepen your understanding of geologic forces and the human efforts that have shaped the landscape and made Wisconsin such a sparkling, natural wonder.

Is It Safe?

Occasionally, travelers ask about the safety of possible underground adventures. Certainly, attractions offering guide services are reasonably safe; however, organized adventure tours are generally inappropriate for younger children. Perhaps the greatest concerns relate to exploring smaller caves on your own. Most sites included are safe for people of all ages, but there are exceptions noted in the listings. For example, several of the caves at Iowa's Maquoketa State Park are best left to adults who enter with at least one other person. Exploring these caves alone is not advised. While serious injury is unlikely, it's possible to slip in mud, fall down a steep incline, or even become stuck in a tight passage.

Most of the sites listed are easily accessible to people with varying levels of physical abilities, and site listings note steep stairways or other possible barriers. Good walking shoes and a light jacket will provide comfort in the larger underground spaces. No other special equipment is required, although you'll want to bring a flashlight if you plan to poke your head into any of the smaller, undeveloped caves. A few adventure-caving opportunities have been included: In these cases, you will need a helmet and several light sources, and trained guides are available to answer questions and help with tour preparation.

WHAT CAN I DISCOVER?

Whatever underground sites you choose to visit, you will be rewarded with new knowledge and often an expanded sense of wonder at what lies so close, buried in darkness beneath your feet. You'll also likely think of new questions to ask: How did the early miners know where to dig? Are there other tunnels located in a certain town or region? And what other mysteries remain unexplored just beneath the surface? Part of the attraction of Wisconsin's underground destinations lies in the questions they provoke. There are always more questions to be asked—and more of the unknown underground world waiting to be explored.

WHAT ABOUT WISCONSIN BATS?

Since detected in Grant County in 2014, white nose syndrome has devastated Wisconsin's hibernating bat populations. In 2015, Wisconsin Department of Natural Resources staff estimated the state had 350,000 to 500,000 hibernating bats. By 2017, surveys showed population decreases of thirty to 100 percent at sites where the fungus had been found two or three years prior, according to the *Milwaukee Journal Sentinel* of May 10, 2017.

First discovered in the United States within a New York cave in 2006, white nose syndrome has spread across the eastern United States and has also been found in the state of Washington. The name "white nose syndrome" comes from the white fuzzy growth sometimes observed on the nose, ears, and wings of infected bats, due to a fungus, *Pseudogymnoascus destructans*. The fungus disrupts the bats' hibernation, causing them to expend energy, dehydrate, and starve. It thrives in humid, cool temperatures in the forty to fifty-five degree range. Wisconsin (and most U.S.) caves and mines fall within this temperature range.

This loss of bat populations is also a major loss for humans. Bats consume millions of bugs and reduce insect populations that harm agriculture and annoy and infect people. Some bats aid in plant pollination, seed dispersal, and scientific advancement. Bat research has improved understanding of hearing, sonar, and blood coagulation, among other advances.

Wisconsin provides a year-round home primarily to four species of insect-eating bats. The little brown bat, which can consume up to 1,000 mosquito-sized insects a night, is the most common, however, it is extremely susceptible to white nose

Eastern pipistrelle in a Southwest Wisconsin cave (Photo: RJ & Linda Miller Photography).

syndrome. The big brown bat is also common in the state, and more tolerant to cold weather than other species. In addition, you can find the northern myotis (also called eastern long-ear) and the eastern pipistrelle. The latter is the smallest Wisconsin bat, with a body measuring less than three inches in length and a wingspan of seven inches or less. Summer visitors include the red, silver-haired, and hoary bat, which all migrate to warmer regions in the winter.

Most year-round species hibernate in mines as well as caves, although sometimes you will find big brown bats wintering in attics and walls. Crystal Cave, for instance, hosts all four year-round species during the cold months. There are approximately150 sites across the state with hibernating bats; sixty percent of these are natural caves. Yet the largest number of hibernating Wisconsin bats are found in mines, according to Jennifer Redell, cave and mine specialist with the Wisconsin Department of Natural Resources. Ninety percent of these are in three mines—Neda, Bay City, and Maiden Rock.

Despite the devastation, there has been some recent good news in the battle against white nose syndrome. There is evidence that some bats survive the disease, including in Europe, from where the disease originally spread to the United States. And some researchers are seeking possible remedies.

Daniel Lindner, a plant pathologist with the U.S. Forest Service in Madison is researching how small doses of ultraviolet light can kill the fungus. Results are promising. A January 2018 report from the USDA Forest Service-Northern Research Station stated: "In the course of genomic analyses of the fungus behind white-nose-syndrome, a devastating disease that has killed millions of bats in North America, US

Forest Service scientists discovered something very surprising: brief exposure to UV-light kills *Pseudogymnoascus destructans*." (www.sciencedaily.com/releases/2018/-01/180102153209.htm)

A team of scientists from the U.S. Forest Service, U.S. Department of Agriculture and the University of New Hampshire published their study in the journal *Nature Communications*, writing, "P. destructans is unable to repair DNA damage caused by UV light, which could lead to novel treatments for the disease." Only a few seconds of moderate exposure from a hand-held UVC light source killed ninety-nine percent of *P. destructans*.

Lindner, a corresponding author on the study, is conducting follow-up research to determine if UV-light can be used as a treatment for bats suffering from white-nose syndrome. The study will measure the survival of little brown bats during hibernation after being treated with UV-light compared to control groups. If successful, the next challenge will be in taking the treatment from a controlled lab into the field.

Many federal, state, and nonprofit organizations are collaborating to address white nose syndrome wherever it occurs. Federally, the U.S. Fish and Wildlife Service leads the U.S. response in combating the disease and is a partner in www.white-nosesyndrome.org, which brings together research and recommendations from all sectors. Other federal agencies involved include the National Park Service, U.S. Forest Service, and U.S. Geological Survey. Several universities, the National Speleological Society, and National Caves Association are among scores of non-federal partners. The Wisconsin Department of Natural Resources is the lead agency in battling white nose syndrome in the state, and the Wisconsin Speleological Society has created an informational page with links to news, videos, and decontamination protocols (www.wisconsincaves.org/WNS).

While most Wisconsinites may be powerless to halt the spread of white nose syndrome, we are not powerless in limiting its impact and improving bats' hibernation environments. While we wait for more good news from researchers like Lindner, we can take several steps to ensure bats' long-term survival:

- If you find dead, sick, or injured bats contact local U.S. Fish and Wildlife Service Field Office or the Wisconsin Department of Natural Resources.

- Do not disturb hibernating bats. Redell says, "There is a season for caving and a season for bats."

- Follow recommended decontamination procedures when visiting mines and caves used by bats. While the fungus is primarily spread from bat to bat, it can survive in the soil of mines and caves and potentially be carried on clothing or equipment.

- Learn more about bats and share what you learn. You may want to attend the annual Wisconsin Bat Festival, coordinated primarily by the Wisconsin Department of Natural Resources Bat Program. The one-day event is held at a different location around the state each year.

You can also install bat houses and volunteer to survey and monitor bat activity in Wisconsin. See: http://wiatri.net/inventory/bats/Volunteer/ or https://dnr.wi.gov/volunteer/animals/Bats.html. University and volunteer researchers, including members of the Wisconsin Speleological Society, have worked to document and protect bat colonies that regularly hibernate in caves and mines. The Wisconsin Department of Natural Resources monitors about 100 bat houses, largely through volunteer assistance.

WHAT ABOUT STORIES AND TALL TALES?

Mystery has always shrouded Wisconsin's underground world, and many legends surround its mines and tunnels. For instance, some stories describe people hiding out in Wisconsin caves, including a boy who reportedly evaded the Civil War draft and a family who tried to escape commitment to an insane asylum. Even Al Capone is said to have tunneled escape routes from a Madison hideout to Lake Mendota. And on May 18, 1934, the *Chicago Tribune* reported that John Dillinger's gang had a hideout in an abandoned mine outside of Cuba City.

Lawbreakers outnumber law-abiding folks in the old stories. According to one, thieves stole a stagecoach full of gold near Blue Mounds. Under hot pursuit, the thieves drove the stagecoach into a large cave entrance. In one version of this story, the entrance collapses with the gold buried inside; in another version, the crooks dynamite it shut. In either case, the gold remains, just waiting for a modern-day explorer to unearth it.

Another legend stars two brothers, recently back from the Klondike gold rush, who were bear hunting on McCaslin Mountain west of Marinette. They chased a bear to the top of a ridge, where the bear disappeared. The brothers heard their footfalls echoing as they walked on the summit and thought perhaps the mountain had mining potential. Looking about, they found flecks of a shiny mineral that they thought might be silver. According to one version of this story (there are many!), the brothers soon realized that the material was not silver, but they hatched a scheme to become rich by defrauding investors in a proposed mine. Another version suggests that the brothers thought the material really was silver and began to tunnel into the mountain in search of the vein, attracting investors in the endeavor. They labored for two years on the tunnel, slowly inching into the hard quartzite. During this time, the two collected a huge sum of money for their enterprise from industrialists, lumber barons, and paper barons in the Fox Valley and Milwaukee. The story concludes with the disappearance of the two brothers—along with the investors' money. One version has the brothers killed by a bear while they were sleeping in the tunnel. Of course the money, in the gold and silver coins of that era, still lies hidden in an old tin cask somewhere on the mountain.

Better-known legends report that people have hidden a variety of other valuables in caves. Bogus Bluff, located above the Lower Wisconsin River, is supposedly named after a gang of counterfeiters who used a cave in the bluff as a hiding place. And another tale recounts how a man found valuable prehistoric skeletons, jewelry, and other artifacts in a cave north of Gotham, which has since been buried.

ARE THERE MANY LOST OR UNDISCOVERED CAVES?

Some caves—and many mines and tunnels—indeed have been buried. Noted photographer H. H. Bennett produced images of shoreline caves accessible by boat in the Wisconsin Dells. Today these caves are underwater, following the construction of a dam on the Wisconsin River. Some caves have been rendered inaccessible by road-building or other construction projects. Many mine shafts have been filled in for safety, and tunnels have collapsed.

Wisconsin's lost and undiscovered underground spaces add to the sense of mystery surrounding any incompletely mapped territory. Becoming an expert on Wisconsin underground is quite a challenge. Even after you have explored all of the sites in this book, many more remain. There is always an unanswered question: Where does this mud-filled side tunnel lead? Or, what lies beneath that sinkhole? Members of the Wisconsin Speleological Society even have added a touch of a legend to their annual meeting—calling it the Hodag Hunt, after that mythical beast originating in Rhinelander.

IS THIS BOOK FOR ME?

This guide is not addressed to experienced cavers. Rather, it is intended to introduce modern-day explorers to the wonders of Wisconsin underground. A basic understanding of the history and geology of its caves, mines, and tunnels can deepen our appreciation of this remarkable state. History can illumine the mine tunnels we enter today, and geology can teach us to read the marks and formations we find written throughout Wisconsin caverns.

Trying to put into words the deep silence of Wisconsin's underground spaces is inevitably imperfect and dilutes to some degree its mystery. The best way to capture this sense of mystery is to search for it yourself—or better, with a friend or your children. Whether you have a day or a week to explore the caves, mines, and tunnels of the Badger State, this book offers signposts to chart your own journeys. The resources and glossary at the back can further help you plot your Wisconsin underground excursions.

SECTION ONE

CAVES

Maribel New Hope Cave (Photo: Kasey Fiske)

Wisconsin is not Kentucky or Missouri or Tennessee, each of which has in the neighborhood of four or five thousand caves; we look at caves differently here. In Kentucky, a cave is not a cave unless it is at least fifty feet long. In Wisconsin, if you can crawl into it, it's a cave.

There are more than forty thousand known caves in the United States, with about a dozen states having more than one thousand caves apiece, while a few have hardly any at all. Wisconsin has more than three hundred known caves, although some of these are barely big enough to house a hibernating bear.

In many areas of Wisconsin, you can find examples of caves caused by weathering, hollowed out by the effects of wind and water erosion. For instance, the shallow caves high in the Mississippi bluffs near La Crosse and the cave beneath the natural bridge at Natural Bridge State Park were caused by weathering and erosion. Often, these caves began at cracks or joints in the rock planes, as is visible in a few of the littoral (sea) caves at the Apostle Islands National Lakeshore. Fissure caves, like the example at Oakfield Ledge State Natural Area, also occur along joint planes.

Most of Wisconsin's caves are located in the southwestern Driftless area, or unglaciated region, of the state. The glaciers that pushed over the eastern two-thirds of Wisconsin crushed and pummeled the landscape, eroding many existing caverns. Over the course of perhaps a million years, glaciers entered the state, finally retreating about ten thousand years ago. The glaciers, which contained embedded sediment and rocks, sometimes grew more than a mile high and exerted tremendous pressure on the earth beneath. When they retreated, they left behind rock and other materials—drift—as well as mounds, hollows, and otherwise marked terrain.

Southwest Wisconsin caves are often solution caves—formed where acidic groundwater has seeped into a crack or joint in the rocks and hollowed out an underground space. Most occur at depths of fifty to seventy-five feet below the surface, although a few are deeper and several lie less than thirty feet underground. Sinkholes—hollows or actual holes in the surface—sometimes reveal the presence of caves, and several Wisconsin caves have been discovered by digging into sinkholes. And once in a while a cave will appear following a mudslide or after a tree topples, revealing an opening below. Certainly, there are yet undiscovered solution caves in Wisconsin.

When new caves are found, they are often mud-filled and require considerable effort to clean out. If they are located in limestone, they many also contain stalactites—compositions that grow downward from the ceiling like icicles; stalagmites—compositions that grow up from the floor like cones; and a variety of other formations, or speleothems. These formations are likely still growing and need to be handled with great care.

Landowners occasionally stumble on a new cave or find one by actively searching along bluff faces or digging into sinkholes. More often, they know of the existence of the cave at the time they purchase the land. A few decades ago, the presence of a cave did not necessarily affect the price of the land. More than one cave owner purchased land prior to 1990 for as little as $300 an acre, particularly when a rugged landscape unsuitable for agriculture was viewed simply as "hunting land." Now, however, more and more people are seeking recreational land with features such as outcrops, steep hillsides, and cascading streams. And sellers are factoring the presence of such features, including caves, into their asking prices. On the other hand, the opportunity to purchase a large cave does not come along every month. One Southwest Wisconsin realtor reported having listed only three significant caves in a seventeen-year period.

Owning a small sandstone cave without formations is like owning any other simple rock attraction, requiring little maintenance or concern. But owning a larger cave, particularly a limestone cave filled with many speleothems, often comes with unplanned obligations. After purchasing a larger cave, you may feel as if you have bought a semipublic attraction. People may know of its location and ask to visit your cave. More than one cave owner has simply grown weary of the multiple requests and tired of seeing cars lined up on the property every weekend. Vandalism and liability issues are other landowner concerns. As a result, the owners of some large caves have gated them or otherwise restricted access.

You still can see some of Wisconsin's largest caves, which have been developed as commercial operations. The commercial caves, or show caves, also offer lighting, a smooth walking surface, and passageways in which you can stand erect.

SHOW CAVES

Wisconsin's show caves are often run as family businesses. Part of the state's premier tourism industry, their owners offer access to these caves for a price. They open their underground treasures to visitors who marvel at the multi-hued formations and caverns that took eons to create.

But this picture is not the whole truth, surely. Just to stay in business, commercial cave owners must protect their treasures from the intentional and unintentional damage of thousands of eager visitors each year. If all visitors touched every formation that tempted them, and if everyone broke off even a small stalactite or stalagmite as a souvenir, eventually there would be no treasures—just empty holes underground.

To stay in business, cave owners must protect their assets by limiting access while offering guided, educational tours by trained staff. They must install electricity, construct safe walkways, and pump or channel excess water. Owners also shoulder the responsibilities of liability insurance, grounds upkeep, and building maintenance.

If the owners want to continue to develop caves, the challenges mount. Owners sometimes talk about their expansion plans and the work they do in the winter months to clean out debris-filled passages and open up new rooms. Cleaning out a passage sometimes involves carefully digging mud or rock away from formations and hauling it out of the cave in buckets—not exactly a glamorous job.

Attesting to the challenges posed by a show cave operation, Lost River Cave reportedly shut down in the mid-1980s due to lack of profits. It is located west of Blue Mounds in Iowa County, and many people still recall touring it.

Despite the challenges, Wisconsin's show cave owners have continued to offer access to an integral piece of the state's natural beauty—a piece much less available to most people than, say, a lake, stream, woodland, or prairie. In the case of a few caves, the owners inherited this opportunity: for instance, Cave of the Mounds has been owned by members of the Brigham family since white settlers first moved into Southwest Wisconsin in the nineteenth century. A few owners purchased their commercial caves. Lured by the hope of earning a living in a rare setting, they responded to the same geologic wonders, beauty, and mystery that attract thousands of visitors each summer.

Two show caves are on public land. Cherney Maribel Caves County Park and Ledge View Nature Center offer their tours with nonprofit and public support, including volunteer maintenance and development efforts.

CAVE OF THE MOUNDS NATIONAL NATURAL LANDMARK
DANE COUNTY

Workers removing limestone from a quarry accidentally blasted into a cave on the Brigham farm west of Mount Horeb in 1939. The explosion tore the face off the quarry, and the blasted rocks surprisingly disappeared from view. Inspecting the site more closely, the astonished workers found a passageway leading to several rooms filled with mineral formations.

The cave acquired its name due to its location on the southern slope of the eastern hill of the two Blue Mounds where Ebenezer Brigham situated his farm in the mid-nineteenth century. A lead miner who came to the region in 1828, Brigham established his diggings and built a smelting furnace and house on the hillside. He was well acquainted with working underground, yet never knew about the jewel lying undisclosed beneath his feet. Much of Brigham's original farm now comprises Blue Mound State Park and Brigham County Park. The two blue hills, of course, also gave the nearby village of Blue Mounds its name.

The relatively recent discovery of the cave has proved a decided advantage. Cave of the Mounds is in a more pristine condition than most—free of graffiti and damage by souvenir hunters.

Day of discovery: Cave of the Mounds (Photo courtesy of Gary K. Soule)

More developed than most other Wisconsin caves, Cave of the Mounds offers approximately 0.25 miles of paved, lighted walkways. An educational tour explains the development of the cave along its "lifeline." This dark crack on the ceiling is a vertical fissure where acidic rain water dripped through the limestone, dissolving the rock and hollowing out the caverns a million or more years ago. Water still drips through the fissure, other cracks, and pore spaces in the rock causing the cave's formations to continue their slow growth cycle: formations grow an average of one inch in one hundred years.

Visitors discover that the tallest stalagmite is almost seventeen feet high from floor to top and encounter several types of formations—for example, the lily-pad and cave-raft stalagmites and the ribbon stalactites that often look like strips of bacon suspended from the ceiling.

Glacier-like, dripping flowstone features a rainbow of color—the translucent white of calcite, the rust color of iron oxide, and the black, blue-black, and gray of manganese oxide.

The play of light and shadow from lights strategically placed along the walkway reveals a constantly shifting panorama of stalactites, stalagmites, and columns: Here, Atlantis rises from the ocean; there, a ship crashes on a barrier reef; and over there, Poseidon himself rises above the dark water. As soon as your mind registers one fantasy, it disappears and is replaced by another imaginatively named formation.

The depth of the cave ranges from twenty to seventy feet below the surface, and as you walk through it, its height varies as well. At one point the largest fossil in the cave looms about twenty feet overhead. The six-foot baby cephalopod, similar to a squid or octopus, died some 400 million years ago.

Since the cave is sealed from the surface, you will see no bats or other wildlife; however, the cave is quite wet. Expect to feel a few drops of water as you proceed along the passages. Rainwater takes several hours to work its way into the cave from the surface, and occasionally low sections must be pumped out after heavy rainfalls.

Cave of the Mounds contains a natural pool, which reflects the largest dome in the cave. Another underground water attraction, the Dream River, twists slowly over flowstone and around stalagmites. It extends roughly 200 feet to the southeast before disappearing into the limestone. The passageway continues another 100 feet or so beyond the river, although this section is closed to visitors.

Between the pool and the river, the magnificent Cathedral Room features rows and clumps of stalactites seemingly welded together like organ pipes. This room has been the site of an occasional wedding ceremony.

Passages seem to extend to infinity.

Visitors view the river rooms from windows installed in a manmade tunnel that parallels a restricted passage filled with delicate speleothems. Another section of the tunnel offers an alternative to claustrophobic visitors daunted by the prospect of traversing the Narrows, where shoulder-brushing stalactites line the walls. Water on either side of the cement walkway through the Narrows looks deep, though the actual depth is only a few inches.

The tunnel provides access to the Gem Room, Centennial Room, and Surprise Cave. The latter, discovered in 1956 during the construction of the last tunnel section, is a small, independent cave a few feet from the main passage. New caves are often discovered adjacent to known caverns.

At one point in the tunnel visitors walk beneath a covered shaft leading up to the surface. Similar to a mine shaft, workers used this opening to remove rock and debris as they constructed the tunnel.

Walking back through the tunnel, visitors get a different kind of caving experience. Underneath the main portion of the cave, a lower level completes an irregular figure eight ending roughly beneath the entrance. The Lower Meanders is a rugged channel, formed not from dripping water but from rushing water eroding and washing through the limestone.

Beyond the base of the figure eight, the cave extends south, ending in the Soda Straw Crawlway. (Soda straws are young, slender stalactites with open centers still unclogged with mineral deposits. Eventually the tip closes, creating a cone shape, or small stalactite.) East of this extension, an exploration team dug a tunnel in the 1970s, however, this blockade of boulders marks the tour's southernmost point.

Researchers generally believe they have completely explored the Cave of the Mounds. Yet they have noted several suspicious low spots in the fields across from the entrance drive, possibly indicating another cave on land still owned by the Brigham family. So far, the family has not extensively explored these sinkholes.

Is there another Surprise Cave lurking underneath the picturesque farmland? Certainly the potential exists for more passages beyond the Dream River, as well as other caves associated with the various sinkholes.

Aboveground, visitors can see several sinkholes, prairie demonstration gardens, and the remnants of a limestone quarry along the Karst View Trail. (Karst refers to topography featuring sinks, ridges, and irregular hills; often, these are honeycombed with solution caves.) South of the parking area, the Oak Valley Loop descends into woodland and savanna, twice crossing Chert Creek. Handouts including a trail guide, Birding checklist, and geologic timeline booklet can enrich your understand of the area's environment and ecology.

School, scout, and other groups take advantage of year-round programming, exploring geology, rock and mineral collecting, orienteering, and environmental education options. Children can mine for gems, hunt for fossils, and even host a birthday party at the cave.

Both below and aboveground, Cave of the Mounds is a Wisconsin natural wonder. The U.S. Department of the Interior and National Park Service designated it a National Natural Landmark in 1988, recognizing it as "a site which possesses exceptional value as an illustration of the nation's natural heritage and contributes to a better understanding of man's environment."

Directions:	Located between Mount Horeb and Blue Mounds, just off U.S. 18/151 on Cave of the Mounds Road/County Highway F. Look for signs.
Seasons/ Hours:	Open year-round. Days and hours vary with the seasons: March 15 through Memorial Day weekend, 10 a.m. to 4 p.m. on weekdays and 9 a.m. to 5 p.m. on weekends; Memorial Day through Labor Day, 9 a.m. to 7 p.m. daily; Labor Day weekend through November 15, 10 a.m. to 4 p.m. on weekdays, and 9 a.m. to 5 p.m. on weekends; November 15 through March 15, by reservation on weekdays and 10 a.m. to 4 p.m. on weekends. Fee. Seasonal and private events are offered throughout the year. Special rates and educational programming are available to classes, scouts, and other groups with advance reservation.
Length:	Tour lasts about an hour, including the approximately 0.25-mile tour and an eight-minute video; busier visitation time may offer self-paced tours, with guides stationed along the route, that allow for more time to explore the cave. Measured length of cave: 1,692 feet.
Precautions:	Light jacket and closed-toe shoes are recommended; temperature is fifty degrees year-round.
Amenities:	Picnic tables, grills, restrooms, hiking trails, gardens, and gift shop. Snack bar shop open seasonally.
Contact:	Cave of the Mounds, Brigham Farm, P.O. Box 148, Blue Mounds, WI 53517. Phone: 608/437-3038. Website: www.caveofthemounds.com.

CHERNEY MARIBEL CAVES COUNTY PARK
MANITOWOC COUNTY

Perhaps more than any other site listed in this volume, Cherney Maribel Caves County Park has evolved significantly since the first edition of Wisconsin Underground appeared in 2000. Thanks to the efforts of the Wisconsin Speleological Society and other volunteers, many cave passages are excavated, accessible, and open for public tours.

Several smaller caves are open to the public whenever the park is open. Larger caves like Maribel New Hope Cave and the Tartarus Cave System are gated but open for public tours from May to October, protecting cave formations and bats who shelter and hibernate there.

The caves are located in the Niagara Escarpment cliff line generally paralleling the West Twin River. The parking area and picnic areas are situated atop the cliff, and visitors hike down to the cave entrances, which generally open in the cliff wall about sixty feet above the river.

Early postcard view of Tartarus Cave entrance (From the collection of Gary K. Soule)

Tartarus Cave entrance today (Photo by Kasey Fiske)

The caves were formed primarily by glacial activity. Through many years of deposition and change, glaciers wore down the land exposing an underlying solid mass of rock—called Niagara Dolomite. The caves formed as the rock decomposed—broken down by the springs, carbonic acid, changing seasons, high volumes of glacial ice melt, and temperature variations.

Volunteers including WSS members are working with Manitowoc County Parks and Planning Commission to systematically excavate glacial sediments and restore the natural beauty of these caves. Counting the three passages now connected within the Tartarus Cave System, the area currently contains ten caves, listed below from south to north:

- Sinkhole Cave
- Cave of Treasures
- Tartarus Cave System (Tartarus, Split Rock, Tunnel)
- Staircase Cave
- Coopers Cave
- Pancake Cave
- Maribel New Hope Cave
- Spring Cave

The most extensive excavation has taken place in the Tartarus Cave System and Maribel New Hope Cave. Tartarus Cave has a long history, dating to at least the early half of the nineteenth century. Early postcards depict visitors at its entrance as early as 1907. Manitowoc County purchased the property for its first park in 1963, and the Wisconsin Speleological Society mapped the cave for the first time, recording a length of thirty-five feet of blocked passage. The WSS began serious excavations in 2004, and the cave length increased to fifty-six feet by 2005. History lovers can find more details by searching for "history of Tartarus" at www.wisconsincaves.org.

Now exceeding 400 feet of excavated passages, the Tartarus Cave System is today a three-entrance cave, with the Tunnel Passage Entrance to the south, the Tartarus Cave Entrance in the middle, and the Split Rock Cave Entrance to the north. Additional passages continue to be excavated, so the final end is not in sight!

Among the several, always accessible caves, Coopers Cave may be the most interesting to casual visitors. It's distinguished by a large rectangular entrance and just a few feet away, a small crevice entrance that makes for excellent photos. Coopers is a square tube, solution cave that is relatively dry with little or no water inside. It extends naturally about twenty feet and has two standing height rooms, with a total length of perhaps one hundred feet.

Discovered on a winter day in 1984, Maribel New Hope Cave was revealed by steam issuing from a pile of talus (broken rocks from the cliff face) covering the entrance. Six years later, Wisconsin Speleological Society member excavated as far as the first room, the Halloween Room. The initial, excavated passages were two-foot-high belly crawls beneath the ceiling. Over the years since the WSS excavated down to the bedrock cave floor here and in another 500-plus feet of walking passage—the longest in eastern Wisconsin. Along the way they found a small natural bridge, a natural column, calcite ledge, ribbons, flowstone and several other formations.

"It's just going to keep going," according to Kasey Fiske, WSS chairman. The organization won't reach the end "in my lifetime."

For more than a century, visitors have flocked to this area for respite—walking through the verdant woods, relaxing along the river, and exploring the caves. Yet only recently has the full extent of these caves been realized.

The seventy-five acre park encompasses the limestone cliff, a section of the West Twin River, and the wooded area in between. Hiking along the trails, you can see walking ferns on the shaded cliff as well as maple, beech, and hemlock. Cedars, eighteen inches to twenty-four inches in diameter, grow at the base of the bluff and throughout the flood plain. Depending on the season, you may see masses of trillium, purple phlox, or

Coopers Cave entrance in Niagara Escarpment

other wildflowers. Birders may want to keep an eye out for the solitary vireo, blackburnian warbler, yellow-bellied flycatcher, and more common species.

Visible from a park observation platform, a gated spring bubbles from the bluff, creating a small waterfall and stream to the river. The spring itself is on private land outside the park boundary. The spring represented one attraction of the historic Maribel Caves Hotel, "an ideal health and summer resort," according to one old brochure. Built in 1900, the hotel was "just the place for the weary to seek rest and comfort" with mineral springs, a bottling plant, and outdoor therapeutic baths.

You can see remnants of the hotel property off the trail leading down from the picnic area toward the river. Although the hotel closed long ago, the current, summertime cave tours draw more than 500 visitors a day. As in the late nineteenth century, Cherney Maribel Caves County Park is still a good place for rest, comfort, and clear thinking.

Directions:	Take I-43 to State Highway 147 (near Maribel), go east one third mile to County Highway R, and then drive about a half mile north to the park.
Seasons/ Hours:	The park is open from dawn to dusk, April through October. The Wisconsin Speleological Society offers public tours on selected weekends from May to October; visit the park website for dates. There is no fee, but donations are accepted. No age restrictions. Dogs (on leash) are permitted.
Length:	Several miles of hiking trails. Maribel New Hope Cave is more than 500 feet long.
Precautions:	Wear good walking shoes or boots and bring a flashlight.
Amenities:	Hiking, skiing, biking, picnicking, fishing, toilets, playground, shelter.
Contact:	Manitowoc County Planning and Park Commission, P.O. Box 610, Manitowoc, WI 54221-0610. Phone: 920/683-4185. Website: https://www.maribelcaves.com/.

CRYSTAL CAVE
PIERCE COUNTY

From the beginning, Crystal Cave has offered adventure to people seeking to explore the earth and test themselves against rock and mud, to rediscover their own inner and physical strengths. Today the cave—located west of Menomonie in Spring Valley—still offers a rugged, exploratory tour for adventurers as well as a more relaxed circuit on paved walkways and ramps. Both trips feature geology and history lessons that you can experience firsthand.

Crystal Cave

Story has it that Crystal Cave was discovered in 1881 by a teenage boy chasing a squirrel about a half mile from his farm home. When the squirrel disappeared down a sinkhole, the boy probed the hole with a stick. When he dropped the stick and it disappeared in the depths, the boy, William R. Vanasse, went home to tell his brother, George.

The next day, the two boys brought a rope and a lantern to the spot and lowered themselves down a "slide" into a clay-and debris-filled room. From there they dropped into the main room on the second of the cave's three levels. In several directions, the boys saw shallow entrances to clay-filled galleries on the upper level.

For decades, Sander's Corner Cave, as it was then called, remained partially filled. Adventurers occasionally visited and explored, but no one realized the size and potential of the Vanasse find—until Henry A. Friede came on the scene in 1941.

An advertising agency manager and amateur geologist from Eau Claire, Friede had been studying caves in the area in hopes of finding one equal to the Cave of the Mounds, discovered two years earlier. He decided that of the several possible sites in the region, the most potential lay in the development of Sander's Corner Cave. In November 1941, a crew began removing the silt and debris, largely completing the job by April of the following year.

Work began on an entrance building, but even before it had been completed, Friede renamed and opened Crystal Cave to the public in June 1942. About four thousand visitors showed up on opening weekend. The new name referred to the quartz crystals found throughout the cave. Since then, more than one million visitors have toured Crystal Cave, which has been further cleaned and explored.

The cave has changed ownership several times. Previous owners Blaze Cunningham and Jean Place opened the cave and surrounding property to exploration by the Wisconsin Speleological Society and Minnesota Speleological Survey, leading to the discovery of additional passages in Crystal Cave and adjacent caves. Today Crystal Cave is the state's longest, with about 4600 feet of passages.

Current owners Eric and Kristin McMaster purchased the cave in 2012 and have continued an emphasis on education combined with entertainment. When visitors walk from the parking lot to the limestone cave building, they pass eight framed displays about cave geologic periods. Another outdoor display describes the property's native pollinator garden, and in-cave displays educate about such topics as fossils and the bats of Crystal Cave.

Located on the edge of the Driftless Area, Crystal Cave lies within dolomite (containing calcium and magnesium carbonate) and features iron ore, flint, and, of course, quartz crystals. There are also two snail-shaped fossils about the size of a nickel—both gastropods from the time the area was part of a giant inland sea.

Visitors also see the Ballroom, the cave's largest chamber, where bats hang out in winter and where more than one couple has exchanged their marriage vows. The Spook Room features unusual "faces" in the walls and is often the kids' favorite. Most kids also enjoy the Story Room, where guides weave a spell by telling such tall tales as that of Cave Man Charley, who once lived in the cave and participated in boat races on an underground river. In the dim depths, with the fantastical formations of Charley and the remainders of his boat clearly visible, even adults almost believe in the myth. Underground, it certainly seems more plausible, than, say, a blue ox.

The walls of the Wish Room are composed of illite, a general term for mica-like clay minerals often found with shales. Clays containing illite are used for makeup, since they absorb facial oils, as well as in construction, china, and medicines. Visitors are invited to place a coin in the soft illite walls and make a wish. The longer their coin sticks to the wall, the more likely their wish will come true. Considering the numerous coins lining these walls, many visitors have had their dreams fulfilled!

Currently the guides use the coins of the Wish Room "to talk about how conservation has changed over the years," Eric McMaster said. Today visitors to any newly opened illite cave passages would never be invited to stick coins into the walls—

anymore than they would be welcome to sign their name to flowstone or break off a stalactite as a memento of their visit.

McMaster has partnered with Santa Clara University and the Wisconsin Department of Natural Resources (DNR) on bat research, including surveying and banding bats. One study involved attaching tiny radio transmitters with an antenna to track individual animals. Another used ultraviolet dust to

Crystal Cave co-owner Eric McMaster in South Portal Cave

determine which bats touched other bats, leading to potential spreading of white nose syndrome. "There's been zero research on the impact of people in caves where there are hibernating bats," McMaster said, noting that bats can get used to people. He reports that on one bat, banded years ago by the University of Minnesota, returned to the same spot on the tour route year after year where it could sometimes be seen by visitors in late spring and early fall.

Ecology efforts extend to the surface, where a seven-acre field near the property entrance is being developed as a pollinator prairie in partnership with the DNR and U.S. Fish and Wildlife Service. There's also a half-mile interpretative trail and 500 maple trees. These are tapped each spring; waist-high plastic piping carries the sap downhill, and its automatically processed using reverse osmosis. The resulting Crystal-Cave branded Maple syrup is for sale in gift shop.

The 100-acre property contains a ravine with four significant cave openings plus several rock shelters. Adventurous visitors can make reservations to take a two-hour wild cave trip through South Portal Cave, hiking down the ravine and entering the cave through a rough wooden door.

South Portal Cave has tight passages, no lights, and an unimproved path. A registration fee includes boots, a hard hat, and headlight. This tour begins with a caving orientation session. Minimum age is fourteen, and children fourteen to eighteen must be accompanied by an adult. Reservations are necessary and there is a maximum of six people per tour. Participants need to sign a liability waiver, be okay with tight spaces, and be physically fit.

Directions:	Located about one mile west of Spring Valley on State Highway 29, approximately fifty miles west of Eau Claire.
Seasons/ Hours:	Open daily: April through May, 10 a.m. through last tour, which departs 4 p.m.; Memorial Day weekend through Labor Day, 9:30 a.m. through last tour, which departs 5 p.m. daily; and September through October, 10 a.m. through last tour, which departs 4 p.m. Fee.
Length:	Tour lasts about one hour. Current tour length of the cave is 2,065 feet.
Precautions:	Light jacket recommended; temperature is fifty degrees year-round. For safety, strollers or backpack style baby carriers are not allowed in the cave; however, soft, front style baby carriers are permitted. Small purses and camera bags may be brought into the cave; lockers are available for larger items.
Amenities:	Picnic tables, restrooms, and gift shop.
Contact	Crystal Cave, W965 State Hwy. 29, Spring Valley, WI 54767. Phone: 715/778-4414. Website: http://www.acoolcave.org/.

LOST RIVER CAVE

Some older readers may recall touring Lost River Cave, not far over the hill from Cave of the Mounds. This failed show cave venture provided a lesson in how not to develop a cave. Uncovered by a road cut a year before the discovery of Cave of the Mounds, its first use was as a roadway drain.

Despite a subsequent Wisconsin Academy of Arts and Sciences survey recommending that the cave had no commercial value, according to a 2012 Wisconsin Speleological Society newsletter report, Lost River Cave was developed into a show cave.

More accurately, Lost River Cave was over developed. Fluorescent spray paint and black lights gave it a 1960s psychedelic look, according to the Wisconsin Speleological Society report. The end of its upper passage was blasted open, and a tunnel was dug to increase its length and reach the site of a nineteenth-century army fort.

None of these efforts worked and the show cave failed. By 1999, the tunnel had largely collapsed, and the collapse and demolition of the ticket office had left the cave wide open, its formations drying out. Visits from raccoons and uninvited partiers caused additional damage.

In the early 2000s the Wisconsin Speleological Society met with the owner and over three years, many people came together to restore the cave—including the Madison Hoofers outing club, Iowa cavers, a landscaping company, an excavating company, the owner, and his neighbors. They closed the tunnel; removed old wiring, rotting stairs, and other show cave remnants; and created a new, lockable entrance using culvert pipes and landscaping materials. They cut a bat-friendly slot in the door.

Thanks to the efforts of many volunteers, the cave has been preserved. And bats once again use Lost River Cave as a hibernation site.

EAGLE CAVE
RICHLAND COUNTY

Known for the amount of onyx it contains, Eagle Cave winds almost a half mile through four levels underneath Southwest Wisconsin's rolling woods and farmland. Located west of Muscoda and north of Blue River, the cave's four levels range from the very shallow first level with tree roots exposed in the ceiling to a passage a full ninety feet beneath the surface.

Discovered in 1849 when Peter Kinder hunted and chased a bear into it, Eagle Cave has been commercially open to the public since 1938. Over time, visitors and development have somewhat changed the nature of the cave, although many multicolored formations, wide passages, and broad rooms remain intact.

Visitors first head to the log office and gift shop to purchase tickets, browse, and get oriented to their surroundings. They then exit the building and follow a short trail to the cave entrance, a doorway into the side of a hill.

A short set of steps leads down into the Thunderbird Room, which is huge by Wisconsin cave standards—roughly forty by sixty feet—and has been used for weddings and parties. Side passages lead to dead ends or down to the undeveloped fourth level of the cave.

A paved walkway at the far end of the room leads into the

Eagle Cave entrance

Light passes through onyx.

main passage, where visitors find
Dino (a baby dinosaur-shaped
formation), an onyx cone
stalagmite, and many creatively
named features. An offshoot, the
Snake Pit, calls up images of Indiana
Jones, as does the Bat Roost. Other
attractions include formations in the
shapes of a shark's head and jaws,
Paul Bunyan's toadstool, and a
potato patch, as well as an eagle.
There are also a white onyx
horseshoe, a witch, a corncob pipe, and a flowstone "frosted" birthday cake—to name a
few of the unique and more fanciful creations.

The cave eagle is not the only connection to its name. Located in Eagle
Township, there once was a community named Eagle Corners, according to cave
historian Gary Soule.

Besides flowstone, stalactites and stalagmites, Eagle Cave features crystals, snail
fossils, and onyx in hues of white, pink and black. Bacon onyx, drapery formations,
cave popcorn, and "caramel corn" cling to the passage walls.

Former cave owners used dynamite to expand the main passage in 1965, resulting
in both a longer, more accessible passage and the partial destruction of some formations. Visitors, however, can still see the impressive remains of a giant stalagmite.

Ten years later, dynamite also opened the Riverbed Room, a thirty-foot-wide,
271-foot-long passage running roughly from the midsection of the cave to an abandoned
rock quarry. Today, a cement-block wall and a steel door block this entrance. Beyond it
is a protected bat hibernaculum and a culvert leading to the surface.

Until the blast occurred, Eagle Cave appeared to end at this point on a rock
ledge. Afterward, explorers clearly saw that the ledge actually was situated above an

Peering into the distance at Eagle Cave

underground river. Following the explosion, the river drained away, leaving the mud-bottomed Riverbed Room open to inspection.

Hollowed by water and time, the Riverbed Room has sparked at least one ghost story. Legend has it that a young couple, Mary and Jonathan, had planned to be married in the Thunderbird Room. Mary went to another room of the cave to dress before the ceremony but never returned. When members of the wedding party searched for her, all they found were her veil and a shoe lying on the ledge above the then unknown underground river.

Sometime later, Jonathan returned to the cave to again search for any sign of his beloved. He, too, disappeared, leaving behind his hat and pipe on the same ledge. Rumor has it that both Mary and Jonathan slipped off the ledge into the river and drowned—and that visitors still occasionally see the ghosts of the two lovers in the Riverbed Room. The room also displays several colors of onyx, as well as crystals, a shell formation in the ceiling, onyx feathers, bacon onyx, and red clay.

During the winter months, scouts and other groups can camp "out" in Eagle Cave. They can get muddy, explore secondary crawling passages on their own, and experience wild caving off the paved tour trail. Some secondary passages are dead ends; others eventually lead back to the main passage. The in-cave exploratory program runs from the last weekend of September to the last weekend of April and is by reservation only. Shorter field trips are also available.

Current owner Weston Hanke continues the family business purchased in 1981 by his parents Dick and Lynda Hanke. He has expanded camping, and seasonal campsites are now available. There are also five cabins, mini golf, and a canoeing on the Wisconsin River.

Directions:	Located off State Highway 60 about six miles west of Muscoda, approximately twelve miles south of Richland Center, and sixty-four miles west of Madison. Look for signs.
Seasons/ Hours:	Guided cave tours are available from Memorial Day weekend through Labor Day, leaving at 10 a.m., 12 p.m., 2 p.m., and 4 p.m. on Thursday, Friday, Saturday, and Sunday. Wild cave tours are also available to the general public during the summer season, reservations required. Fee.
Length:	Tour lasts about one hour. Measured length of main and secondary passages: 2,445 feet.
Precautions:	Light jacket recommended; temperature is about fifty degrees year-round. May be muddy.
Amenities:	Campground, toilets, hiking trails, guided horseback trail rides, fishing in Little Blackhawk Lake on the grounds, and a lodge for group meals.
Contact:	Eagle Cave, 16320 Cavern Lane, Blue River, WI 53518. Phone: 608/537-2988. Website: http://www.eaglecave.net/.

KICKAPOO CAVERNS
CRAWFORD COUNTY

From a Native American shelter to a prospective mine site to a boy's adventure land to a tourist attraction to a preserved bat hibernaculum, Kickapoo Caverns has a long and many faceted history. If time were a kaleidoscope and each twist of the cylinder brought a new decade into view, the Caverns' history would present constantly changing hues and patterns. Used as early as the 1600s by Native Americans, according to cave historian Gary Soule, the Caverns also hosted prospecting lead miners in the 1800s, boys searching for adventure in the early 1900s, and entrepreneurs seeking to develop and share this natural resource. At different times it was variously called Kickapoo Crystal Caverns, Kickapoo Caverns, and Goblin Cave.

The last private owners of the Caverns, Ray and Delores Gaidowski (and later their daughter Carole Gaidowski Porter) purchased the property in 1962. They restored

Looking down on the tour route through the Cathedral Room (Postcard from the collection of Gary K. Soule)

the rundown property; renamed it Kickapoo Indian Caverns; and offered commercial, guided tours. The family added Native American artifacts and crafts for display and sale in the building previously erected at the cave entrance. Over the years they also expanded and improved the underground tours.

If you had visited the Caverns in 2000, the year of *Wisconsin Underground*'s first edition, you might have been greeted by the beat of a Native American drum as you stepped from your car in the parking lot. When you opened the squeaky door and stepped across the threshold into the museum and shop, you entered the murky past. Inside, the year was 1850. Arrowheads, scrapers, and amulets glinted dully in the shop's glass display cases. Shelves of Native American artifacts as well as newly made pots, moccasins, jewelry, and other items for sale line the plain wood walls. The merchandise represented the craftsmanship of many tribes across the United States, gathered on trips by the Caverns' owners.

Cave tours in 2000 began through a doorway in the small shop, with a steep descent down a cement staircase into limestone caverns dripping with stalactites and stalagmites and still growing ever so slowly at the rate of approximately one half inch every 100 years.

At the base of the stairs, ancient poles leaned against the wall and chips of rock littered a flat-surfaced stone, to demonstrate that hundreds of years ago Native Americans crafted tools and weapons here. The poles may have been used for drying animal hides.

Evidence of ancient visitors of another species could be seen high overhead. The fossilized thigh bone and ball joint of a mastodon were visible in the ceiling.

In the in the nineteenth century, soldiers from Fort Crawford in Prairie du Chien rediscovered these caverns while searching for lead in the region. Later explorers found miners' picks, shovels, and cartridge boxes, which were sometimes used to carry ore samples out of new diggings. However, when no lead was found here, it became a popular destination for picnickers. Names and dates scratched in the cave date back to 1846.

Guides would point to onyx formations that, like clouds on a summer day, fired the imagination All kinds of animals and objects—for instance, a cheeseburger, an eight-legged giraffe, a pig, and even a complete Jack-and-the-Beanstalk scene—could be visually. In the beam of a flashlight, the cool stones twisted and turned, transforming into the swirling rides of a carnival at night. The columns moved inexorably downward, like stone whirlpools to the center of the earth.

The deepest point of the caverns, the Cathedral Room, is about forty feet high and 160 feet underground. The cave system likely extends another 260 feet or so farther down, with the lower portions being entirely underwater.

On the return walk, you saw different creatures and objects in the smooth formations. The pig on the way down turned into a buffalo on the way up. Visitors sometimes also saw many bats snoozing peacefully on the ceilings of several chambers.

Bats, it would turn out, would be vital in the next chapter of the Caverns' story.

After Ray and Delores Gaidowski divorced in 1999 and Ray died in 2001, Delores continued to run the site on her own. Declining attendance, however, was a problem, and finding guides became an increasing challenge. Eventually Delores was left to do much of the work on her own. A knee injury forced her to close the caverns in 2007, Soule reported, though she later reopened it, with tours offered when possible until 2011. Delores Gaidowski passed away in 2014.

Daughter Carole Porter sought to honor her mother's wishes to keep the property in its natural state. In 2017 she sold the eighty-tree acres with the Caverns to the Mississippi Valley Conservancy, which renamed it "Kickapoo Caverns." The acquisition followed a year-long fundraising campaign, with donors including the Prairie du Chien Rod and Gun Club, Wauzeka Lions Club, Whitetails Unlimited, Wisconsin DNR, the Paul E. Stry Foundation, and John C. Bock Foundation among others.

"Throughout the campaign, many local residents shared their stories of touring the cavern as kids. Memorable experiences such as these have a lasting impact. They help fuel our efforts to protect land for the future," said the Conservancy's executive director, Carol Abrahamzon, in a news release at the time of the acquisition.

The cavern provides a significant hibernaculum for two federally and state-threatened bat species and the Conservancy manages it specifically for the protection of the bats, including closing the cave to tours during bat hibernation season. Making use of the existing development of the cave, the Conservancy plans summer cave tours focused on bat and cave education; check the Conservancy's website for dates and times, as well as for tour guide volunteer opportunities.

At the same time, the Conservancy will open the acreage to year-round hiking, bird-watching, seasonal cross-country skiing, hunting and other outdoor recreational activities. Guided hikes, volunteer work days, and other events will welcome all ages to experience and enjoy the site. In addition to the Caverns, the property is home to a prairie full of colorful wildflowers reminiscent of the habitat found in Crawford County 200 years ago. There are also limestone cliffs, rock outcrops, and oak savanna with an understory of pink and purple shooting stars. The site is located within the boundary of the Lower Kickapoo River Important Bird Area and provides excellent bird-watching opportunities, with nesting pairs of the state threatened cerulean warbler, ovenbirds, wood thrush, and other migratory birds.

Directions:	Off Highway 60, fifteen miles southeast of Prairie du Chien. Driving northwest from Wauzeka on County Highway N, follow the signs and angle right onto Horses, a narrow, ascending road. Look for signs.
Seasons/ Hours:	Contact Mississippi Valley Conservancy (below).
Length:	The Wisconsin Speleogical Society surveyed Kickapoo Caverns and the nearby Wauzeka Cave in 1961, reported Soule, resulting in a total of about 1400 feet in the Kickapoo-Wauzeka Cavern System.
Precautions:	No strollers. Light jacket recommended; temperature is forty-eight degrees year-round.
Amenities:	Year-round hiking, bird-watching, seasonal cross-country skiing, hunting and other outdoor recreational activities.
Contact:	Mississippi Valley Conservancy, P.O. Box 2611, 1309 Norplex Drive, Ste. 9, La Crosse, WI 54602; Phone: 608 784-3606. Website: https://www.mississippivalleyconservancy.org.

LEDGE VIEW NATURE CENTER
CALUMET COUNTY

Ledge View Nature Center offers the best of both worlds: an opportunity to take a walking tour of a relatively undeveloped cave with optional crawlways and/or a chance to experience a wilder environment—crawling required. Naturalists lead regularly scheduled tours from May to November and discuss cave formation, geology, and biology, as well as the human history of the caves.

Representing a public-private partnership, Ledge View is a Calumet County Park developed largely through philanthropic contributions, including the work of the Wisconsin Speleological Society, which cleared out many cave passages. The park contains two cave systems—Carolyn's Caverns and Montgomery Cave.

Carolyn's Caverns includes Bat Room, Dave's Sink, Keith's Karst, and Wayne's World, as well as Mothers Cave. Visitors can choose from a Carolyn's Tour or a combination Carolyn's and Mothers Cave tour. Mothers Cave is unexcavated and contains crawling-only passages.

Although Ledge View offers an opportunity for anyone of any age to enjoy a true caving adventure, it is especially welcoming to kids. This hands-on children's museum of caving takes visitors beyond the paved pathways, permanent lighting, and water control measures of the state's more developed caves. If the weather aboveground has been rainy, the cave is guaranteed to be wet and muddy. Ledge View's caves run approximately thirty to thirty-five feet below the surface and up to several hundred feet in length within the Niagara escarpment dolomite.

A guided exploration of Montgomery Cave, known since the time of the Civil War, begins with a descent down a steep metal stairway through a sinkhole. On the way down, the lucky visitor may see a phoebe rise from her nest in a small shelf of the rock ledge, revealing several small, pale eggs.

Montgomery Cave is a solution cave, formed when acidic rainwater entered a crack in the dolomite and, over thousands of years, chemically dissolved the rock around the crack. This crack became the lifeline of the cave and is still visible on the surface just north of the cave entrance, as well as within the cave itself. Montgomery features circular chimneys, calcite crystal formations, and side passageways.

Carolyn's Caverns was discovered in 1986 by Carolyn Schleis and other members of the Wisconsin Speleological Society who dug through a sinkhole in the park. They found two rooms plugged with rocks and mud. The Wisconsin Conservation Corps dug out more than eight tons of debris during the summer of 1986.

Visitors today descend a seventeen-foot ladder to access the large, first room. Visible in the first and second rooms are examples of cave coral and cave drapery hanging from the ceiling. Stalactites and flowstone also appear. Carolyn's Caverns offers walking passages with optional crawling experiences along the tour route.

The entrance to Mother's Cave, discovered by Norb Kox on Mother's Day in 1986, is located at the base of a ledge. Explorers can observe flowstone, fossils, and a large stalactite. Mother's Cave is a winter home to garter and fox snakes, as well as several types of bats. In addition, visitors often observe cave spiders and chirpless cave crickets. This tour concludes with a belly crawl and exit through the Squeeze. (As a prerequisite to entering this cave, visitors must demonstrate their ability to wriggle through a replica of a tight cave passage—termed "the box" and located in the Nature Center).

Above ground, Ledge View's 105 acres are home to a wide variety of wildlife. Bird watchers have recorded nesting pairs of about forty species, including scarlet tanagers, indigo buntings, red-eyed vireos, and cedar waxwings. Many more species have taken refuge at Ledge View during spring and fall migrations.

Ledge View offers numerous attractions in addition to the caves. A wildflower garden lures hordes of butterflies, and a network of trails invites hikers, bikers, skiers,

and snowshoers. A sixty-foot observation tower provides a birds-eye view of the terrain. Besides the cave tours, year-round educational programming features such topics as astronomy, edible plants, and maple syrup production. The Nature Center itself contains animal exhibits and space for group presentations.

Ledge View's recreated escarpment with wildlife

Yet the cave tours remain the most significant feature of the park and no doubt will be attracting students—young and old—for years to come. In fact, Ledge View still contains a number of unplumbed sinkholes and unexplored passages; so future tours may be all the more intriguing.

Even now, watching a stream of mud-covered young adults straggle up the trail from the caves at the end of a tour is absorbing, like a video of old-time miners emerging from the earth at the end of their shift. What you see is mostly the eyes—and the mud.

Unlike the commercial caves, the Ledge View tours give us a chance to challenge ourselves with an immediacy unattainable in more developed caves. Your feet push against the rocks, you feel the water seep through your clothes, and you follow the beam of your light through the passages until you finally emerge into daylight—covered with the signs of your success.

Directions:	Located south of Chilton off of County Highway G.
Seasons/ Hours:	Call for reservations. Walk-in and adventure tours of Carolyn's Caverns and Mothers Cave are scheduled from May through November. Minimum age for Carolyn's tour is five, with a parent, children need to be able to use a ladder safely. Minimum age for Carolyn's and Mothers Cave tour is eight, with a parent. Mothers Cave tour is all crawling. Fee.
Length:	The cave tours last about two hours.
Precautions:	Entering the caves requires no special preparation, although the average temperature is about fifty degrees. Taking an adventure tour, however, requires coveralls or a long-sleeved shirt (a sweatshirt is ideal) and means getting covered in mud. Bring a flashlight. Wear a knit cap to protect your head from bumps and sturdy shoes or rubber boots.
Amenities:	Hiking, dog sledding, snowshoeing, cross-country skiing, maple syrup making, picnicking, biking, restrooms, nature center.
Contact:	Ledge View Nature Center, P.O. Box 54, W2348 Short Rd., Chilton, WI 53014-9673. Phone: 920/849-7094. Website: http://www.ledgeviewnaturecenter.org/.

WILD CAVES

While all of Wisconsin's commercial caves are limestone and/or dolostone solution caves with stalactites, stalagmites, and other formations, the caves accessible on public lands offer a variety of types and features, including litoral caves and crevices barely large enough for a well-fed raccoon. Smaller than the commercial caves, some of those on public lands might be scorned by a Kentucky caver as not worth investigating. Yet searching them out can offer pleasant hiking or boating, opportunities to learn about the state's flora and fauna, and majestic bluff-top views.

There's often the added adventure of finding them on your own without the assistance of a tour guide. Walking down a forested path in a state park, for example, you may wonder about the small cave or rock shelter ahead. You scan the landscape as soon as you round a curve or crest a hill, searching for a sign of its existence. Whether you locate a cave on your own and find not a soul nearby, or you share the experience with a friend of your family, the rewards total more than identifying a certain excavation in the earth. They include the breeze of a summer's day, the changing colors of sandstone in sunlight, and the scent of wild roses on the wind.

So pull that creased map out of the glove compartment and let your adventure begin.

OWNING YOUR OWN CAVE

Once or twice in a decade, you might find a real estate ad like this one, which appeared in 1999: "800-foot long cave, 70 mostly wooded acres, hay meadow, deer/turkey, new gravel drive, 5 miles north of Wisconsin River. Asking $105,000."

An older couple was selling part of their farm, which had been in the family for many years. Their cave opens up in a field, just below the crest of a hill. The entrance is wide and slopes gently downward. It's an easily accessible cave and a popular destination for area cavers.

"Scads of university students have gone through it," said the farmer. "Sometimes, five or ten vehicles would be lined up in the driveway on a weekend." After a while, the farm couple simply "got tired of people asking and visiting."

Former Eagle Cave owner Dick Hanke observed that owners of larger caves sometimes restrict entrance out of concern for vandalism or liability issues. While it may be fun to own your own cave—just think of the Halloween possibilities—there are also responsibilities.

Of course, most of the state's caves are much smaller. Many Southwest Wisconsin landowners rarely think about the caves on their land, which may be little more than animal dens or small rock shelters. You may see land with a small cave or two for sale fairly regularly.

A decade or two ago, wooded land with steep hillsides and a cave could be purchased very reasonably, sometimes for only a few hundred dollars an acre, since the land was viewed as too poor for agriculture. Now, however, land with outcroppings and other rock formations fetches as respectable a price as homesteading acreage. Yet, it's still possible to occasionally find a cave property for sale if you want one.

APOSTLE ISLANDS NATIONAL LAKESHORE
ASHLAND AND BAYFIELD COUNTIES

At Wisconsin's northernmost point, the Apostle Islands National Lakeshore includes twenty-one of the twenty-two Apostle Islands and twelve miles of shore, bluff, and woods on the mainland. People come to the lakeshore area to hike, picnic, sail, scuba dive, and sea kayak; they also come to visit the sea caves carved into the cliffs near Squaw Bay on the Lake Superior shoreline, on the north shore of Devils Island, and at Swallow Point on Sand Island. The largest Apostle Island, Madeline Island, also contains sea caves in Big Bay State Park. The truly adventurous have been known to go cliff jumping above the sea caves at Big Bay, into water that hovers in the fifty-degree range in the summer.

Centuries of wave action, freezing, and thawing have sculpted these shorelines, creating extensive littoral caves with carved arches, vaulted chambers, and honey-combed passageways up to fifty feet or so into the red sandstone bluffs. This sandstone, the Devils Island Formation, was created more than one billion years ago, when rivers

Water- and wind-carved littoral (sea) caves (Photo: Bayfield Chamber and Visitor Bureau)

carried sandy sediments from Minnesota to the basin now containing the Apostle Islands. The sediments slowly filled the basin, forming a sand flat covered with shallow ponds and channels. These fine-grained and ripple-marked deposits eventually became the easily eroded sandstone known as the Devils Island Formation. Another key feature is that this formation is composed of very thin layers; in other words, it is thinly bedded, which also aids erosion.

You can see these ever-evolving caves from a distance by tour boat, or up close during calm conditions in a sea kayak or smaller boat designed for Lake Superior waters. You also can see the mainland caves on foot—either from a bluff-top hiking trail or during colder winters when the Lake Superior ice is solid enough to walk on.

The Apostle Islands Cruise Service provides a good introduction to the sea caves; once you've taken a half-day tour, you're better prepared to explore the islands in more depth on your own. Headquartered in Bayfield, the Apostle Islands Cruise Service offers its Grand Tour of all the islands, including the Devils Island sea caves, and an evening cruise to the Squaw Bay sea caves on the western side of the Bayfield Peninsula. This is a great time of day to view these caves—at sunset with the slanting rays illuminating the caves from the west. There's also a Ship Wrecks, Sea Caves, and Lighthouses Tour for folks interested in exploring aboveground as well as underground attractions. In addition, several kayak outfitters offer guided tours of the Apostle Islands.

If you would like to hike to the sea caves at Squaw Bay via the ice in winter, check with the Apostle Islands National Lakeshore Headquarters on ice conditions in January and February (contact information below). In recent years, warm winters have limited opportunities to explore these caves. Hikers who are able to make the trek, however,

Squaw Bay caves in winter (Photo: Bayfield Chamber and Visitor Bureau)

will be rewarded with a wonderland of icicles, frozen waterfall, and intricate, natural ice sculptures. You can most easily reach the caves from Meyers Beach, near the west end of National Lakeshore's mainland unit. The turnoff to Meyers Road is about eighteen miles west of Bayfield off of State Highway 13. The GPS address is: 90500 Meyers Road. There is a parking area and stairs to the beach/ice at the end of Meyers Road. The caves begin a little more than one mile north of the beach stairs.

During the rest of the year, you also can see the Squaw Bay sea caves from a promontory along the Lake Superior shore to the northeast. Since 1999, a two-mile section of the Lakeshore Trail has been open to hikers. This segment begins at the Meyers Road picnic area, a sandstone cliff offering a spectacular view of the mainland sea caves.

Once you've seen the sea caves, be sure to budget at least a couple of hours to wandering around Bayfield, Walking through historic downtown Bayfield provides many enticements to the curious traveler, from memorable restaurants to creative gifts and a slew of seasonal events. Of course, if you just want to hang out, there are plenty of opportunities to de-stress and relax.

To the east, Pictured Rocks Cruises offer tours of Lake Superior bluffs including sea caves from Munising, Michigan. Two-and-a-half to three-hour tours follow about forty miles of shoreline. (Phone: (906/387-2379. Website: www.picturedrocks.com.)

When you drive south from Bayfield, you may want to look for a Wisconsin Historical Marker noting a manmade underground structure. Look for the marker in Ashland at a parking lot on Washington Avenue at its intersection with North Broad Street, at 37 North Broad Street. The marker commemorates a Bayfield apple cellar, constructed by William Knight in the 1920s.

Directions:	Visitor center is located off of State Highway 13 in Bayfield.
Seasons/ Hours:	Visitor center is open daily from 8 a.m. to 4:30 p.m., May 1 to Memorial Day; 8 a.m. to 6 p.m., Memorial Day through Labor Day; 8 a.m. to 5 p.m. Labor Day through the last weekend in October; and Monday through Friday from 8 a.m. to 4:30 p.m., the rest of the year. Closed on Thanksgiving, December 25, and January 1. The Apostle Islands Cruise Service generally operates daily from May 15 through October 10. Fee.
Length:	Some of the sea caves extend as many as fifty feet into the bluffs. A boat tour to the sea caves takes several hours. A walking tour—on the frozen lake in winter or on a bluff overlooking the caves in summer—takes approximately one hour.

Precautions:	Summer evening temperatures are cool, averaging about fifty-five degrees. Summer weather can change rapidly, and the National Park Service does not recommend small open boats for inter-island use. (You may want to tow a smaller boat and use it to explore the caves in calm seas.) Biting insects are common from early May to mid-August. Black bears are found on several islands, so you need to keep campsites clean and hang all food. Even though wells are provided on some islands, you should be prepared to boil or filter lake water. In winter, lake ice conditions vary; extreme caution is required in crossing the ice. If you are planning a winter trip to the mainland caves, call the Apostle Islands Ice Line at 715/779-3397 for current ice conditions or check the Apostle Islands National Lakeshore Facebook page: www.facebook.com/apostleislandsnationallakeshore/. Watch for cracks in the ice and falling ice and rock; carry an ice bar to test its thickness.
Amenities:	Bayfield and Ashland offer many intriguing attractions. One of these is the Lake Superior Big Top Chautauqua, a performing arts organization with a 900-seat tent theater, which presents concerts, plays, lectures, and original, illuminated historical musicals. Located three miles south of Bayfield, the Chautauqua also presents the Wisconsin Public Radio program, Tent Show Radio. Also of interest are lighthouse tours, charter fishing trips, and ferry trips to Madeline Island. The largest Apostle Island has been developed and is not part of the National Lakeshore. You can reach it via a twenty-minute car-ferry ride from Bayfield. Its attractions include Big Bay State Park, Big Bay Town Park, sea caves, and the Wisconsin Historical Society's Madeline Island Historical Museum.
Contact:	Apostle Island National Lakeshore, 415 Washington Ave., Bayfield, WI 54814. Phone: 715/779-3397. Website: www.nps.gov/apis/index.htm. Contact: Big Bay State Park, 2402 Hagen Rd., La Pointe, WI 54850. Phone: 715-747-6425. Website: http://dnr.wi.gov/topic/parks/name/bigbay/. Contact: Apostle Island Cruise Service, 2 N. Front St., Bayfield, WI 54814. Phone: 800/323-7619. Website: http://www.apostleisland.com/.

BLUE MOUND STATE PARK
DANE COUNTY

While visitors cannot enter the caves beneath Blue Mound State Park, they can see photos of several in the nature center. Currently, staff enter the caves to survey bat populations every other year or so.

Visitors can also view sinkholes where the roofs of several caves have collapsed. A sign marks one sinkhole on the John Minix Trail near the park's northern boundary. Others (some are gated) can be spotted near other trails, especially along the south side of the mound during leaf-off conditions.

Niagara dolomite—the same rock that composes the Niagara Escarpment in eastern Wisconsin—caps Blue Mound, as well as Platte Mound, Belmont Mound, and Sinsinawa Mound. Rivers and wind have eroded the Niagara dolomite and underlying

*Cave beneath Blue Mound State Park
(Photo: Wisconsin Department of Natural
Resources)*

layers of sandstone and limestone from most of Southwest Wisconsin over millions of years.

The other key to this Driftless Area of rivers, valleys, hills, ridges and rock outcrops is its lack of glacial impact. In a quirk of nature, the glaciers that moved across the state up to about 10,000 years ago all bypassed southwestern Wisconsin, southeastern Minnesota, northwestern Illinois, and northeastern Iowa, leaving karst topography and preserving more underground spaces. Karst is "a landscape created when water dissolves rocks," according to the Wisconsin Geological and Natural History Survey (https://wgnhs.uwex.edu/water-environment/karst-sinkholes/). In Southeast Wisconsin, glacial fill lies on top of the karst.

In 1909 Edward Lange completed his University of Wisconsin undergraduate thesis titled, *Original Work on the Caves of the Driftless Area of Southwestern Wisconsin*. His thesis analyzed several caves, including the "Blue Mounds Cave," located about one mile northwest of the Blue Mounds railroad station. He described the entrance as a sink, "a funnel-shaped depression about 60 feet across the top and reaching about 20 feet below" the surface. This cave measured 250 feet long, with an average passage width of five-and-a-half feet. Average height was five feet, however, a few places required stooping or crawling to negotiate. Even as early as 1909, Lange noted broken stalactites and stalagmites, damaged, he surmised, "by some careless persons who were unable to carry them off."

Possibly Lange's most interesting observations relate to "evidence that caverns are quite common in this region." He mentioned another one five miles north and then states, "The existence of other caverns is proved by the fact that well-drillers report [their] drill often falls several feet." Thirty years before the discovery of Cave of the Mounds, Lange wrote: "That there should be caverns in this section is further indicated by the numerous 'sinks' which exist in this region. Several of these occur on the farm of Mr. Charles Brigham."

Current Blue Mound State Park manager, Kevin Swenson, suggests a good modern-day thesis topic might involve using ground penetrating radar to map the park's underground cave system. Just an idea, waiting for a researcher.

Directions:	North of Blue Mounds, about twenty-five miles west of Madison off U.S. Hwy. 18/151. Turn north on County F and then left on County ID into Blue Mounds. Continue west on ID about a half mile to Mounds Road. Turn right (north) and follow Mounds Road, which becomes Mounds Park Road after you leave the village. The park is one mile north of the intersection of County ID and Mounds Road. Vehicle admission sticker required.
Seasons/ Hours:	Open year-round from 6 a.m. to 11 p.m.
Precautions:	No public access to caves.
Amenities:	Nature center, nature trail, amphitheater, restrooms, two observation towers, hiking, outdoor swimming pool, camping, picnicking, bicycling, mountain biking, hunting and trapping, snowshoeing, sledding, cross-country skiing.
Contact:	Blue Mound State Park, 4350 Mounds Park Rd., Blue Mounds, WI 53517. Phone: 608/437-5711. Website: https://dnr.wi.gov/topic/parks/name/bluemound/.

BEAR CAVES STATE NATURAL AREA

Finding a hibernating bear in Bear Caves State Natural Area seems about as likely as finding a cave there. Truth be told, there are no caves, though there are piles of large, round boulders with spaces between and among the stones. While a bear— or a human—can squeeze among the boulders in some places, light almost always filters in. The boulders average four to six feet in diameter, though some are larger.

Dating back 10,000 years or more, the pink granite boulder train formed between two lobes of the Wisconsin Glacier. As the lobes melted they pushed against one another, and the boulders were likely formed and concentrated along this junction during strong runoff. Gravel and smaller rocks between the boulders were likely washed away during furious runoff.

Bear Caves is owned by Langlade County and managed through its Forestry and Recreation Department. To get there, drive to the intersection of State Highways 64 and 55 in Langlade County and then go north on Hwy. 55 about three and a half miles to a town road. The town road is Old Highway 55 and today leads to the town sanitary disposal site. Park at the town road and walk across Hwy. 55 to an unimproved access road. Walk west along the unimproved access road approximately two tenths of a mile. Look for a line of piled granite boulders, or mounds of boulders to your left.

Website: http://dnr.wi.gov/topic/Lands/naturalareas/index.asp?SNA=286.

The boulders at Bear Caves State Natural Area

CAVE POINT COUNTY PARK
DOOR COUNTY

Cave Point County Park

Pitted as if from a recent hailstorm, the bluffs and ledges along Lake Michigan at Cave Point County Park lie bare and vulnerable. Worn away by centuries of wind and waves, the dolomite cliffs have been carved into unusual formations, and caves penetrate deep into the bluffs. Unlike the sea caves of the Apostle Islands National Lakeshore, these caves are mostly underwater. Yet walking on the rocky ledges, you know the caves are there, hidden beneath you. The booming of the waves hurling against their walls drowns out other sounds, their power almost ominous.

Surrounded by Whitefish Dunes State Park, Cave Point is one of nineteen parks in the Door County parks system. All are located on the shoreline.

Cave Point is part of the Niagara Escarpment, a thick line of dolomite layers that runs from Niagara Falls across Ontario and Michigan, entering Wisconsin in the Door County Peninsula. One side of the ridge features a gentle upward slope, the other a vertical cliff. Cave Point makes geologic change visible; you can clearly see the impact of wind, water, and temperature on this land over many centuries. With the wind in

On the edge of the ledge

your face and the thundering waves pounding the rock layers beneath your feet, you can feel the dominion of nature in this place. With a strong wind from the east, the waves sometimes leap thirty feet into the air as they crash against the cliffs. Photographers take note: In winter the sparkling spray freezes, overlaying rocks, trees, and outcrops with slick, dazzling ice.

A bit dangerous at any time of year, in summertime Cave Point draws risk-taking swimmers who dive off the cliffs into the chilly Lake Michigan waters. Precautions should be taken to learn the temperature and depth of the water below before taking this plunge.

Adventurers can gain a different perspective on Cave Point by kayak, either on their own or through an outfitter such as DC Adrift (Door County Kayak Tours); website: https://dcadrift.com/. On calm days, the waterline exploration provides an opportunity to view a longer length of the cave-studded cliffs. DC Adrift also offers paddleboard tours and rentals.

The cliffs, caves, and rocky shoreline are the main attractions of the nineteen-acre county park; however, it also offers picnicking, interpretative signage on the geologic history of Cave Point, and hiking. Be on the lookout for sinkholes leading into the caves beneath your feet, and the geysers spouting from them on windy days. A spur trail from the parking lot leads to the Black Trail, which runs through the hardwood forests back from the shoreline and into the surrounding Whitefish Dunes State Park.

The Black Trail loops around the less well-traveled northern section of the state park, offers frequent wildlife sightings, and connects with the Brachiopod Trail. This mile-and-a-half nature trail is a comprehensive outdoor classroom. It presents information about early marine animals including brachiopods—invertebrates with two-part shells and two arms, generally on either side of the mouth. Information stations also cover area wildlife, plant succession, and dunes formation.

Directions:	From Sturgeon Bay, take State Highway 57 north through Valmy to County Highway WD. Watch for signs. This park is located within Whitefish Dunes State Park.
Seasons/ Hours:	Open year-round. Free.
Length:	The hiking trail on the top of the bluffs is a half mile long and connects to more than a dozen miles of trails in Whitefish Dunes State Park.
Precautions:	Steep cliffs.
Amenities:	Hiking, picnic tables, grills, restrooms, kayaking off shore. Gazebo can be reserved for special events.
Contact:	Door County Parks Department, 3538 Park Drive, Sturgeon Bay, WI 54235. Phone: 920/746-9959. Website: www.doorcounty.com.

DEVIL'S LAKE STATE PARK
SAUK COUNTY

Elephant Cave at Devil's Lake State Park was not named for its size. The tunnel-like opening shrinks from a height of five feet or so at the entrance to barely more than two feet, and the passage is taller than it is wide. Beyond the short entrance passage is a small rock-floored room—and that's the extent of Elephant Cave.

Named for Elephant Rock on the park's East Bluff Trail, approximately a quarter mile from the last parking lot on the lake's north shore, the cave is near the top of one of the 500-foot cliffs overlooking clear, spring-fed Devil's Lake. Flanked by bluffs, the deep lake is the jewel of the park, a diamond set in a quartzite bracelet.

The quartzite bluffs formed a billion years ago, when sand was deposited by rivers draining into shallow seas. As the sand accumulated, it first formed porous sandstone, and then nonporous quartzite. Eventually the seas withdrew, and at some point the land buckled to form the north and south ranges of the Baraboo Hills. The depression between these two ranges was filled with softer sediments that eroded over the eons, partly by an ancient rive or rivers cutting through the area.

Entrance to Elephant Cave

Then, about 15,000 years ago, the Wisconsin Glacier moved into the region, depositing a ridge of rocks and gravel at the terminal moraine, effectively plugging the gaps at either end of the depression and forming Devil's Lake.

Today, many people come to the park to hike the bluffs and see Balanced Rock, Devil's Doorway, and other unlikely formations, as well as participate in water activities in and on the lake. Though is less crowded during the offseason, the number of visitors to the park doubled from 2002 to 2016, growing from more than 1.3 million to close to 2.6 million.

Directions:	From the south or east on I-90/94, take State Highway 33 west about fifteen miles to Baraboo. Turn left (south) at the second traffic light onto Broadway. At the second traffic circle, go left onto County Road DL and drive two miles to the park. From the northwest on I 90/94, go right (south) at exit 92. Take US Highway 12 East about ten miles to exit 219. Turn left onto South Boulevard. Turn right onto State Highway 136 and follow it about three miles to the park entrance. From the south on US Highway 12, take exit 219. Turn right onto South Boulevard. Turn right onto State Highway 136 and follow it about three miles to the park entrance.
Seasons/ Hours:	Open year-round, 6 a.m. to 11 p.m. Visitor center opens at 8 a.m. in summer, 8:30 a.m. the rest of the year; it closes at 11 p.m. in the summer and at 4 p.m. the rest of the year, except for longer hours Friday through Sunday during the spring and fall. Pass required.

Length:	The cave extends perhaps twenty feet; the trail to the cave is approximately a quarter mile from the last parking lot on the lake's north shore.
Precautions:	Bring a flashlight.
Amenities:	Biking, swimming, camping, canoeing, fishing/ice fishing, scuba diving, picnicking, rock climbing, cross-country skiing, toilets, three pet swim areas, and a nature center.
Contact:	Devil's Lake State Park, S5975 Park Rd., Baraboo, WI 53913-9299. Phone: 608/356-8301. Website: http://dnr.wi.gov/topic/parks/name/devilslake/.

H. H. BENNETT

Photographer H. H. Bennett (1843 – 1908) captured many iconic images of early Wisconsin Dells' scenery. The image of his son Ashley leaping the chasm to Stand Rock, which documented Bennett's stop-action camera skills, is likely the most familiar. But Bennett also photographed several caves that are no longer accessible, due to the dam constructed a year after his death at the Dells—then called Kilbourn City. The dam divided the river into the Upper Dells and Lower Dells, raised the level of the Wisconsin River around the town, and flooded many sandstone caves and formations.

Thanks to Bennett's photos, you can view several of these on the Wisconsin Historical Society's website: https://www.wisconsinhistory.org/, which offers more than 80,000 images. Search for "Boat Cave," "Cave of Dark Waters," or "Black Hawk's Cave" to find a few of Bennett's images. Or, search for "caves" to find more than one hundred cave depictions, including postcards, advertisements, and stereo views created by a variety of photographers.

FONFEREK'S GLEN COUNTY PARK
BROWN COUNTY

Hidden behind farmland and encroaching development, Fonferek's Glen offers a quick stretch and getaway within two miles of I-43 east of De Pere. After a short drive down Memory Lane, you can park before a barn, walk around the barn, and follow the blue arrows about 100 yards to a thirty-foot waterfall. Cross Bower Creek just above the falls on rocks (stepping stones) or in low water on rock shelves, which are twenty yards or so upstream. There's a rock shelter to the left of the falls as you face the falls. Over many centuries, the waterfall has been retreating into the bluff, hollowing out a layer of chert in the dolomite.

Downstream from the waterfall, a natural bridge and small cave are visible, at about the same distance from the top of the cliff as the waterfall. Wind, rain, and changing temperatures also have hollowed these formations out of the same cherty layer of dolomite. While the cave is not easily accessible, it is visible—most clearly from the trail at the other end of the glen, leading from the end of another dead-end road one block north of Memory Lane.

Located in the Town of Ledgeview, the park totals seventy-four acres including thirty acres of former agricultural fields replanted with native trees and prairie. Much of

Undercut waterfall at Fonferek's Glen

the park is a natural conservancy area with steep cliffs, falling rock, rugged terrain, and generally difficult footing.

Directions:	Exit I-43 on County Highway MM. Drive one and three quarters mile to Memory Lane. Fonferek's Glen is located at the end of Memory Lane.
Seasons/ Hours:	Open year round, 8 a.m. to sunset. Free.
Length:	The glen is an 800-foot contour.
Precautions:	The park features steep drop-offs, falling rocks, and rugged terrain. Pets not allowed.
Amenities:	Green Bay offers many other parks, recreational activities, shops, and restaurants. For instance, Bay Shore Park, located eleven miles north of the city on State Highway 57, offers hiking along the bluff and shoreline of Green Bay.
Contact:	Brown County Park Department, P.O. Box 23600, Green Bay, WI 54305-3600; physical address: Barkhausen Waterfowl Preserve (follow signs to the Main Park Office), 2024 Lakeview Dr., Suamico WI 54173. Phone: 920/448-6242.

GOVERNOR DODGE STATE PARK
IOWA COUNTY

The sandstone shelters in the bluffs of Governor Dodge State Park could tell many a tale if only they could speak. If these walls could talk, they might relay the joys and disappointment of untold generations of humans who sought winter refuge in the clefts and hollows now contained in the park, from prehistoric peoples to twentieth-century farm families.

Excavations have revealed winter camps established by prehistoric peoples in the caves and overhangs as much as eight millennia ago. In particular, archaeological investigations at Deer Cove Rock Shelter—so named because deer were seen taking refuge there—provided evidence of early inhabitants. Artifacts, such as projectile points, scrapers, and choppers, discovered in excavated layers were used by both Archaic (8000 to 500 B.C.) and Woodland (500 B.C. to 1600 A.D.) period peoples. Many Fox, Sauk and Ho Chunk called this Driftless area home until lead miners and other European settlers invaded the hills and valleys.

Deer Cove Rock Shelter is near the Deer Cove Picnic area, on the drive from the Park entrance toward Cox Hollow Lake, past Enee Point Picnic area and the boat launch. A kiosk in the picnic area describes the archeology of the shelter, accessible via a very short trail. Two park caves, both formed in St. Peters sandstone, are accessible to hikers.

You can walk to the larger cave via a one-mile extension off the Meadow Valley Trail, periodically catching glimpses of Twin Valley Lake as you hike around and halfway up a bluff. Also known as Thomas' Cave, it features an approximate three-foot-high entrance passage leading to a large circular room. The high-ceilinged room conveniently contains a number of boulders to perch on—all in all, a great setting for telling a ghost story or two! Although the trail to the cave is well marked, not all trails appear on the park maps, so it's possible to mistake one trail for another, particularly during the offseason when there may be few other hikers around to direct you. Of course, some visitors claim that getting lost adds to the adventure—or maybe not.

The Small Cave is sometimes a tour destination for the site naturalist, supported by the Friends of Governor Dodge State Park. This cave lies beyond and above a rock shelter northeast of Twin Valley Campground. Though less well marked than the trail to Thomas' Cave, the route to the Small Cave, also via the Meadow Valley Trail, is easy enough to find. Once you reach the rock shelter, a short climb leads to the entrance in the bluff. It opens into a narrow room that can hold perhaps ten people. A tiny tunnel extends into the bluff, but is filled with rubble and has not been excavated.

Gates have been installed at the entrances of both caves. Closed in the offseason, they protect hibernating bats from human disturbance.

Hikers can also explore other in-ground and underground sites throughout the park. There's an old quarry in the park where fossils can sometimes be seen and a small overhang adjacent to Stephens Falls, named for an early farm family who contributed land to the park. Nearby a stone springhouse partially dug into the hillside still stands. Constructed in the 1850s, the building once housed a water-powered pump that carried water to the Stephens house and farm; the family also used the structure for cool storage. Another of the park's three springhouses is also dug into the hillside. Located off the Lost Canyon Trail, the Wilson springhouse beneath the summer kitchen of the family's farmhouse once both cool milked and preserved food.

Like many of Wisconsin's state parks, Governor Dodge exudes both human history in addition to the earth's geology. As you walk its trails, you may stumble on the remnants of a stone foundation, spy a fragment of barbed wire, or even spot an arrowhead—all reminders that humans have lived in these hills and valleys for centuries. Remember to leave these remnants in place for the next visitors to spot and enjoy, too.

The path to Small Cave

Open bat gate at Small Cave

Directions:	Located on State Highway 23, two miles north of Dodgeville.
Seasons/ Hours:	Open year-round, 6 a.m. to 11 p.m. A naturalist is on duty from Memorial Day weekend through August. Vehicle admission sticker required.
Length:	The largest cave extends perhaps thirty feet into the bluff. Hiking time to and from the large cave is less than two hours from the parking area. A guided hike to the small cave takes ninety minutes.
Precautions:	Don't forget a flashlight, so you can explore the caves; there are occasional puddles in the entry passage and room of the large cave.
Amenities:	Biking, boating, canoeing, camping, fishing/ice fishing, hiking, horseback riding, cross-country skiing, snowmobiling, sledding, hunting, trapping, nature center, toilets.
Contact:	Governor Dodge State Park, 4175 State Highway 23, Dodgeville, WI 53533. Phone: 608/935-2315. Website: http://dnr.wi.gov/topic/parks/name/govdodge.

HIGH CLIFF STATE PARK
CALUMET COUNTY

While there are no dark caverns to explore at High Point State Park, you can find many fissures and cracks in the forty-foot cliffs of the Niagara Escarpment here, as well as remnants of historic limestone quarry operations.

Trails in the 1,187-acre park—including the 125-acre area High Cliff Escarpment State Natural Area contained with the state park—feature up-close experiences of the ledges and long-range views of Lake Winnebago. Within the natural area, the talus slope below the escarpment here is composed mostly of small rocks, along with some larger limestone boulders. Sugar maple, basswood, ash, elm, hackberry, and butternut can also be found on the slope.

A limestone quarry and kilns operated here from 1895 to 1956, The Western Lime and Cement Company supplied limestone for brick mortar and crushed into gravel, as well as lime for plaster and cement and as a soil additive to reduce acidity. Up to forty people worked here, for example, drillers, a blasting specialist, stone crushers, teamsters, barrel makers, and a blacksmith. The "company town" consisted of sixteen houses for workers, a tavern, and a store with a post office, telegraph office and company office. The store and ruins of the kiln can still be seen in the park today.

In addition, a number of 1500-year-old effigy mounds are visible on Indian Mound Trail. The 0.6-mile, limestone surfaced trail interprets the cultural history of the mound builders. From the same trailhead off the park road, the Red Bird Trail traverses the top of the escarpment, offering an observation tower with grand views of Lake Winnebago and a thirteen-foot-tall Red Bird statue.

Directions:	From the intersection of State Highway 49 and County Highway Z (east of Horicon Marsh), go north on County Highway Z for two miles. Turn right on Breakneck Road and drive to the top of the ledge. There is a small parking area on the left about a half mile from the intersection of Breakneck Road and County Highway Z.
Seasons/ Hours:	Open year-round, 6 .m. to 11 p.m. Park office hours vary by season. Labor Day through mid-May, Tuesdays through Sundays 10 a.m. to 4 p.m. A self-pay station is available for vehicle admission sticker (required) and camping fees when the park office is closed. Hiking trails not maintained in winter.
Precautions:	Trails can be steep, slippery, and treacherous, with sharp drop-offs at the cliff edge.

Amenities:	Marina with 100 rentable slips, concessions, General Store Museum, hiking, camping, biking, fishing, archery-only hunting and trapping, swimming, boating, kayaking, canoeing, horseback riding, picnic areas and playgrounds, two pet picnic areas, cross-country skiing, winter fat tire biking, snowshoeing, snowmobiling
Contact:	Wisconsin Department of Natural Resources, N7630 State Park Rd Sherwood WI 54169. Phone: 920/989-1106. Website: http://dnr.wi.gov/topic/parks/name/highcliff/.

HORSESHOE BAY CAVE
DOOR COUNTY

Discovered by two hunters who noticed water emerging from approximately 129 feet below the top of the Niagara Escarpment in 1896, Horseshoe Bay Cave is the state's second-longest cavern. (Crystal Cave currently has the record for length of surveyed passages.) The Door County cave runs beneath the Horseshoe Bay Golf Course, with Door County owning the entrance and land above the first seventy-five feet. The surveyed length of the cave totals more than 3,000 feet, with additional potential passageways yet unexplored. An underground river carved out these passages in the dolomitic limestone of the Niagara Escarpment an estimated 60,000 years ago, and this river still flows through the lower sections of the cave today. One room is 350 feet high; another features a forty-five-foot underground waterfall.

Variously known as Tecumseh Cave, and Murphy Cave, and Egg Harbor Cave, Horseshoe Bay Cave was first mapped in 1939 and 1940 when Dr. J Harlen Bretz and his students from the University of Chicago surveyed its first 500 feet. Over the next several decades local cavers and the Wisconsin Speleological Society surveyed additional passages and its underground river was discovered in 1978—and nicknamed the Mississippi. To get through the river passages, cavers don wetsuits and go for a fifty-two-foot blind swim before reaching the Big Room, which features a fifty-five-foot-high domed ceiling. To protect these passageways and their bat populations, the cave was gated in 1986.

As is true for several other Wisconsin caves, myths abound. But, no, Tecumseh never escaped into this cave, and there is only one entrance and exit.

For several years Wisconsin Speleological Society member Gary Soule advocated for the county to acquire the cave and it finally purchased the pasture across the road from Frank E. Murphy County Park for added parking. The nearby cave entrance also came to county ownership thanks to a land swap with Horseshoe Bay Golf Club in 2011.

Three years later the Door County Board approved a management plan for Horseshoe Bay Cave. It calls for controlled access and little excavation. (Removing glacial fill from the floor would allow easier access and expanded educational opportunities.)

Currently the cave is open to the public for guided tours one summer weekend a year and groups can make special arrangements for tours, which all traverse only the first section of the cave.

Folks interested in this cave can find additional information in a framed display at Frank E. Murphy County Park and on a kiosk display in Egg Harbor's Harbor View Park. The latter, which discusses the region's karst landscape, is one of several along the sixty-six-mile Door County Coastal Byway along Hwy. 42/57, a designated Wisconsin Scenic Byway.

Directions:	Approximately two and a half miles south of Egg Harbor, across the road and through the field from Frank E. Murphy County Park, 7119 Bay Shore Dr., Egg Harbor, WI 54209.
Seasons/ Hours:	Open one weekend a year and for groups by special arrangement. Contact the Door County Parks Department.
Length:	A guided tour of the publicly accessible section of the cave takes forty-five minutes to an hour. More than 3,000 feet of cave passages have been surveyed.
Precautions:	Bending and crawling required, often in wet and muddy conditions. Uneven surface but no vertical climbs or drops. Long-sleeved shirt, jeans, and good walking shoes recommended. Youths under age sixteen must be accompanied by an adult age eighteen or older.
Amenities:	The nearby county park offers restrooms and contains a framed display about Horseshoe Bay Cave. Door County offers something for everyone—from parks to shopping and entertainment,.
Contact:	Door County Parks Department, 3538 Park Dr., Sturgeon Bay, WI 54235. Phone: 920/746-9959. Website: http://map.co.door.wi.us/parks.

Entrance to Horseshoe Bay Cave with bat gate

CAVE MAPS

Translating the three-dimensional routes of an underground cave system into a readable, two-dimensional map requires skills, experience, and tools; and cave surveying is a key function of speleological organizations. Offered here are two examples. First, a fairly traditional map of Horseshoe Bay Cave demonstrates the complexity in surveying height, depth, and underwater features, in addition to simple direction. It also presents a standard NSS (National Speleological Society) map legend and a profile view.

The second map of the Tartarus Cave System at Cherney Maribel Caves County Park used technological survey tools to portray the discovered connection between two previously separate caves within the Niagara Escarpment. A "drip line" is the line in the ground at the cave entrance formed by drops falling from the rock overhead. The drip line is technically the starting point by which a cave's length is measured.

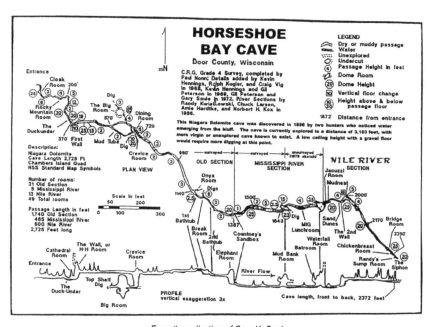

From the collection of Gary K. Soule

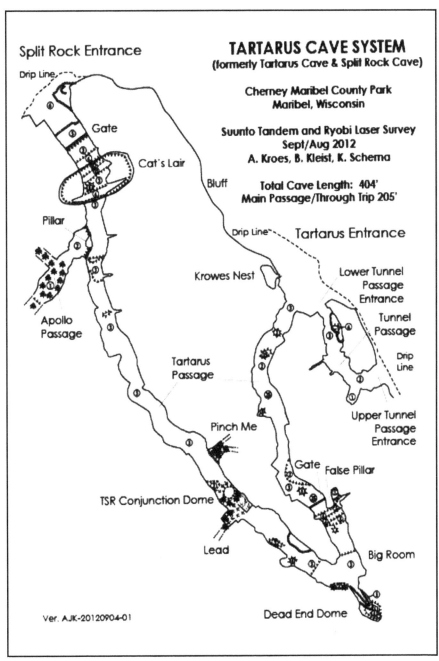

Split Rock Entrance

TARTARUS CAVE SYSTEM
(formerly Tartarus Cave & Split Rock Cave)

Cherney Maribel County Park
Maribel, Wisconsin

Suunto Tandem and Ryobi Laser Survey
Sept/Aug 2012
A. Kroes, B. Kleist, K. Scherna

Total Cave Length: 404'
Main Passage/Through Trip 205'

Drip Line

Gate

Cat's Lair

Bluff

Pillar

Drip Line

Tartarus Entrance

Krowes Nest

Lower Tunnel
Passage
Entrance

Tunnel
Passage

Apollo
Passage

Drip
Line

Tartarus
Passage

Upper Tunnel
Passage
Entrance

Pinch Me

Gate   False Pillar

TSR Conjunction Dome

Lead

Big Room

Ver. AJK-20120904-01

Dead End Dome

From the collection of Gary K. Soule

HOUGHTON FALLS STATE NATURAL AREA
BAYFIELD COUNTY

The Houghton Falls State Natural Area is also the Houghton Falls Nature Preserve, created in 2010 through a collaboration of private landowners, the Town of Bayview, conservation organizations, the Wisconsin Department of Natural Resource's Knowles Nelson Stewardship Fund, and the National Oceanic and Atmospheric Administration's (NOAA) Coastal and Estuarine Land Conservation Program. The seventy-six-acre preserve protects an ancient sandstone gorge along Lake Superior south of Bayfield.

A stream spills over the exposed sandstone and then falls sixty feet to the lake. Upstream, a narrow trail leads visitors through Echo Dells, which features water-carved cliffs and small caves. The Dells sustains hemlock, yellow birch, and mountain maple, along with a variety of ferns, thimbleberry, wood sorrel, and small enchanter's nightshade. The preserve also helps maintain unfragmented, undeveloped Lake Superior shoreline, which supports both resident and migratory birds. At the end of the trail, visitors can catch views of Chequamegon Bay and the Apostle Islands.

Several other state natural areas feature overhangs that may have once sheltered people, however, many lack developed trails to these features.

Houghton Falls State Natural Area trail (Photo: Thomas Meyer, Wisconsin Department of Natural Resources)

Directions:	About two and a half miles north of Washburn on State Hwy. 13, turn east on Houghton Falls Road and drive a half mile to the trailhead and parking area south of the road. Parking on the road is not permitted. If the lot is full, the Town of Bayview requests that visitors return later, to avoid overuse of the preserve.
Seasons/ Hours:	Approximately sunrise to sunset. There is an automatic gate, and tickets are issued to visitors in the area after hours. During the winter, the area closes at 4:30 p.m.
Length:	Trail is one-and-a-half miles long.
Precautions:	Bikes not allowed. Private property; stay on the trail.
Amenities:	Amenities: Bayfield County offers many other attractions worth a visit, from the Apostle Islands National Lakeshore to the Wisconsin Historical Society's Madeline Island Museum to Big Top Chautauqua.
Contact:	Websites: http://dnr.wi.gov/topic/Lands/naturalareas/index.asp?SNA=638 and http://www.brcland.org/houghton-falls-nature-preserve.html.

LEDGE COUNTY PARK
DODGE COUNTY

Situated between Mayville and Beaver Dam, Ledge County Park resembles Oakfield Ledge State Natural Area and High Cliff State Park: all feature sections of the Niagara Escarpment and small crevices and caves in the limestone cliff. Ledge County Park adds the advantages of a developed playground, picnic area, and campground.

From the park entrance, you can drive to a campground as well as picnic and play areas located atop the ledge; or you can drive down to the base of the cliff, where another picnic area and shelter occupy a broad lawn. Near the edge of the lower parking area, a monumental bur oak sways lightly in the breeze. A sign proclaims "Contemplation Tree"; and benches surround it, inviting you to pause in the shade of the venerable oak.

Other park amenities invite you to get moving. Hiking trails wind throughout the eighty-three-acre park, and the trail at the top of the forty-foot ledge provides a grand overlook of Horicon Marsh to the west. While several trails lead up from the base of the ledge to the top, including one just south of the Contemplation Tree, easier access to Cave Trail atop the ledge is from the upper parking area, which remains open year-round. As the Niagara Escarpment has eroded and broken down, the cracks and crevices among the sections of broken cliff face have created a number of small caves, often with both entrances and exits. Water, ice, and leaves can make climbing treacherous, so proceed with caution, particularly from fall through spring.

Directions:	From State Highway 33 east of Beaver Dam, turn north on County Highway TW. Then turn east (right) on Raasch's Hill Road, driving three quarters mile to Park Road and turning north (left). Access Cave Trail from parking area atop the ledge.
Seasons/ Hours:	Open year-round except during gun deer season in November. Closed to vehicular traffic in winter. Free.
Length:	The small crevices and caves extend fifteen to twenty feet into the bluff.
Precautions:	There are steep bluffs and drop-offs. Wear sturdy shoes or boots and bring a flashlight to explore the longer cracks and passages.
Amenities:	Camping (April through October), hiking, picnicking, playground, toilets.
Contact:	Dodge County Land Resources and Parks Department, 127 E. Oak St., Juneau, WI 53039. Phone: 920/386-3700.

LOST CREEK FALLS
BAYFIELD COUNTY

Want to walk behind a waterfall? Head to Lost Creek Falls southwest of Cornucopia.

The highlight of the county's Lost Creek Falls Scenic Area, the falls can be reached via a one-and-a-half-mile hike through a hardwood forest, accessible from May through October. The falls drops about eight feet over an undercut sandstone ledge, with smaller cascades above and below this point. The 334-acre scenic area also features a snowmobile trail, remnants of old logging roads, and sections of several creeks.

Directions:	From Cornucopia, follow County C for one and a half miles south to Trail Drive. Turn right (west) on Trail Drive to reach the parking area and trailhead on the left.
Seasons/ Hours:	Dawn to dusk, from May through October.
Length:	The trail is approximately one-and-a-half miles long.
Precautions:	This is a relatively easy, gravel trail with boardwalks.
Amenities:	Bayfield County offers incredible, additional natural and manmade attractions, from the Apostle Islands National Lakeshore to the Wisconsin Historical Society's Madeline Island Museum to Big Top Chautauqua.
Contact:	Bayfield County Forestry Department, 117 E. 5th St., Washburn, 54891. Phone: 715/373–6114. Website: www.bayfieldcounty.org.

MONTEREY CAVE
ROCK COUNTY

Monterey Cave, viewed from the park across the Rock River

Who would expect to find a cave smack in the middle of a Wisconsin city, its opening clearly visible to all who pass by? Yet a small cave opens above the Rock River near Janesville's Monterey Park. Only seventeen feet long, the cave pushes into Monterey Rock—formerly called "Big Rock"—which directed Native Americans and early nineteenth-century travelers to a shallow, fordable area in the river.

According to the historical marker atop the rock, it gave Rock County its name, although some sources suggest different name originations. In 1835 Joshua and William Holmes, Jr., John Inman, and George Follmer built the first log cabin nearby, beginning the county's first permanent settlement.

Though marred by graffiti inside, the cave showcases the area's geology. Monterey Cave developed in St. Peter Sandstone and its ceiling runs up to a cap of Platteville dolomite. Ceiling height varies from roughly eight to twelve feet.

If you're interested in an urban hike, the National Ice Age Trail runs through Janesville, crossing the Rock River not far east of Monterey Park.

Directions:	Located off Riverside Drive, just west of Monterey Park, 501 Rockport Rd., Janesville, with parking available at the park.
Seasons/ Hours:	Open year round.
Length:	The cave is seventeen feet long.
Precautions:	Beware of slippery conditions from water or ice.
Amenities:	Park offers paved trail, fishing, restrooms, sports stadium.
Contact:	Monterey Park phone: (608) 755-3025. Website: http://www.janesvillecvb.com/ things_to_do/details/4720/225663/Monterey_Rock.

NATURAL BRIDGE STATE PARK
SAUK COUNTY

The largest natural bridge in the state cuts a wide arc through a Wisconsin woodland and harbors a broad rock shelter or cave near its sandstone base. Archaeologists have shown the shelter provided human refuge several millennia before European explorers arrived in the area. A partial excavation of the site in the mid-1950s revealed signs of human habitation, possibly dating to as early as between 9000 B.C. and 8000 B.C. Archaeologists also uncovered the remains of more than fifty mammal species, including many either now vanished or very rare in this region—for example, passenger pigeon, elk, bobcat, fisher, marten, and mountain lion.

Now protected by a rail fence, the shelter is still easily visible from the Indian Moccasin Nature Trail, which loops from the parking lot to the bridge and an overlook that provides a wide-angle view of the wooded valley. (Circle to the right on the loop to reach the bridge by the shortest distance, about a quarter mile from the parking lot.) Sandstone walls facing the shelter along the trail somewhat hinder photo possibilities.

A total of about four miles of trails provide a variety of easy hiking opportunities across gentle slopes, woodland, and open areas. An offshoot of the nature trail connects with a path leading to a log house and smokehouse, located west of the parking area. Across County Highway C from the parking lot, the Whitetail Hiking Trail meanders through woodlands and prairie. Except for the area immediately

Natural Bridge with rock shelter (Photo: RJ & Linda Miller Photography)

surrounding the natural bridge and rock shelter, much of the park's 500-plus acres is former cropland. Look for a map of the park at a kiosk near the parking area. There is no park office.

Directions:	Located northwest of Sauk City, about nine miles west of U.S. 12 on County Highway C.
Seasons/ Hours:	Open year-round from 6 a.m. to 11 p.m. Vehicle admission sticker required.
Length:	The twenty-five-foot wide bridge measures thirty-five feet high at the top of the arch, which is less than four feet wide. The rock shelter is more than seven feet high and measures sixty feet wide and thirty feet deep.
Precautions:	The bridge is an easy quarter-mile walk from the parking lot, including a gentle slope and some steps.
Amenities:	Picnicking, toilets, hiking, hunting and trapping, snowshoeing, and cross-country skiing—however, there are no groomed ski trails.
Contact:	Natural Bridge State Park, E7792 County Hwy. C, North Freedom, WI 53951. Phone: 608-356-8301. Website: http://dnr.wi.gov/topic/parks/name/naturalbridge/.

Oakfield Ledge State Natural Area
Fond du Lac County

Drive up Breakneck Road in southern Fond du Lac County, and you may think you are in another country. Jutting above the surrounding farmlands, a several-mile-long section of the Niagara Escarpment shows dark gray against a winter-white landscape, somewhat resembling the arched back of a dinosaur, or maybe Nessie rising from the depths of the loch. Even when covered with mid-summer vegetation, it's hard to miss the forty-foot vertical cliff, rugged with rock ledges and outcroppings.

Crevices and fissures formed at the face of the cliff when glacial ice moved parallel to the limestone escarpment, dug into the underlying layers, and then retreated. With the support of the ice removed, the vertical faces of the escarpment tended to lean outward, creating crevices up to fifty feet wide along the joint planes.

Not far from where Breakneck Road ascends the escarpment there is a spring, sheltered by rocks, and a balanced rock atop a pedestal more than thirty feet high. Less than a quarter mile to the north is a fissure cave you can enter by passing through a narrow crevice at the base of the bluff.

Top of the ledge

From the parking area, follow the trail across the prairie to the woods. You will soon be walking atop a ledge trail lined with cracks and crevices, many with perseverant cedars growing on them. Oak and hickory nevertheless predominate on the top of the escarpment, while basswood and sugar maple grow at the base. You also can find walking ferns, which grow only on limestone exposures. Dissimilar in appearance to other ferns because of its unserrated leaves, the walking fern grows along a rock face by putting out new plants where the tip of a leaf touches the limestone surface.

Lacking the development of trails and picnic areas of most state parks, Oakfield Ledge attracts few visitors. Yet its unusual formations and features offer excellent opportunities for exploring the environment of the escarpment. It also provides a grand wide-angle view of the surrounding fields, farms, and woodlots.

Directions:	From the intersection of State Highway 49 and County Highway Z (east of Horicon Marsh), go north on County Highway Z for two miles. Turn right on Breakneck Road and drive to the top of the ledge. There is a small parking area on the left about a half mile from the intersection of Breakneck Road and County Highway Z.
Seasons/ Hours:	Open year-round; however, the parking area is not plowed in winter. Free.
Length:	The forty-acre natural area includes a 200-foot section of the Niagara Escarpment.
Precautions:	The trail along the top of the ledge is not overly difficult, but it runs adjacent to the edge of the cliff.
Amenities:	The area is about a half-hour drive from Fond du Lac, which offers numerous shops, restaurants, and other attractions.
Contact:	Wisconsin Department of Natural Resources, 1210 N. Palmatory St., Horicon, WI 53032. Phone: 920/387-7860. Website: http://dnr.wi.gov/topic/Lands/ naturalareas/index.asp?SNA=190.

PENINSULA STATE PARK
DOOR COUNTY

If you visited Peninsula State Park in 1920, you might have climbed a wooden staircase to reach the entrance to Eagle Cave, one of the largest littoral caves on the Great Lakes, according to cave historian Gary Soule. The cave extends forty-one feet into the Niagara Escarpment and has a ten-foot-wide entrance about twenty-five feet above the current level of Green Bay. It's visible from a boat on the lake and from the Eagle Bluff Trail, which leads along the bluff just above the rock-strewn beach.

Eagle Cave opens in the bluff high above Green Bay.
(Photo from the collection of Gary K. Soule)

Eagle Bluff, of course, is part of the Niagara Escarpment, and the terraces, or ledges, in this case are old shorelines. Crossed with tree roots, the rugged Eagle Bluff Trail provides a close-up view of the dolomite cliff and several small caves hollowed out of the eroding dolomite. Eagle Cave looms high above on the vertical wall and today is inaccessible, except for bats and birds.

Once you've explored Eagle Bluff Trail, there's a lot more to see above ground at Peninsula State Park. Roads and trails on the top of the cliff provide

Photo taken in 1919 shows top of staircase to entrance
(Photo from the collection of Gary K. Soule)

panoramic views of the bay, and you can golf, visit an historic lighthouse, and take in a well-respected theater performance. However, you can no longer ascend the seventy-five-foot Eagle Tower at the other end of the park, which was removed in 2016 due to its poor condition. The Friends of Peninsula State Park is raising funds to reconstruct a new tower in compliance with the Americans with Disabilities Act and current construction codes.

Looking up at the entrance today

The second oldest of Wisconsin's state parks, established in 1910, Peninsula is also one of the most popular, logging more than one million visits annually. The 3,776-acre wilderness contains forests, meadows, and wetlands, as well as the shoreline.

Depending on the season, you can find a variety of wildflowers—for instance, dwarf lake iris, fringed polygala, yellow lady's slipper orchid, and wood lily. In addition, Peninsula has become known as a great place to watch the spring warbler migration; and redstarts, black-throated green warblers, and pileated woodpeckers nest in the park. It's no wonder that so many humans migrate there each year, too.

Directions:	Located off of State Highway 42, near Fish Creek.
Seasons/ Hours:	Open year-round, 6 a.m. to 11 p.m. Vehicle admission sticker required.
Length:	Tiny accessible caves; one large cave visible, along a two-mile trail.
Precautions:	Challenging, difficult trail.
Amenities:	Boating, biking, camping, hiking, picnicking, playgrounds, fishing, swimming, cross-country skiing, snowmobiling, showshoeing, and sledding. There are also an eighteen-hole golf course, nature center, the 1868 Eagle Bluff Lighthouse, and Northern Sky Theater performances in summer.
Contact	Peninsula State Park, 9462 Shore Rd., Fish Creek, WI 54212. Phone: 920/868—3258. Website: http://dnr.wi.gov/topic/parks/name/peninsula/.

POTAWATOMI STATE PARK
DOOR COUNTY

Commemorated in the name of its Ancient Shores Nature Trail, Potawatomi State Park gives evidence of ancient glacial lake levels and shorelines. Small littoral caves can be seen in the park, and the three largest (still relatively small) are a short hike north of the boat launch parking lot. Follow the unmarked, wooded shoreline trail 200 to 300 yards until it turns inland. Proceed several hundred feet and then veer left to the base of the bluff. The three caves are in a line part way up the bluff at an elevation of about 600 feet—formed when the glacial lake was much higher than Lake Michigan today.

Eroded into the Niagara dolomite, the three caves vary in length from twenty-six feet to thirty-one feet. The easternmost is the longest and L-shaped, with a maximum height of sixteen feet. This cave and the westernmost particularly exhibit the straight walls and square corners sometimes seen along the fissures of the Niagara Escarpment.

Potawatomi contains the eastern trail head of the Ice Age Trail near the observation tower. Located entirely in Wisconsin, the Ice Age Trail is a 1,000-mile National Scenic Trail wending along the edge of the last continental glacier in the state.

Looking out from one of Potawatomi State Park's small caves

Away from the shore, forests of sugar maple, basswood, birth, and beech, as well as white and red pine cover most of Potawatomi's 1,200 acres. It features typical Wisconsin wildlife, including deer, raccoons, fox, gray squirrels, opossums, skunks and chipmunks. Also watch for pileated woodpeckers in the woods and gulls and terns along the shoreline. The Friends of Potawatomi State Park support a naturalist, and a variety of programs is offered during the summer season.

Gary Soule in a Potawatomi State Park cave

Directions:	Located on County PD, 2.4 miles north off State Highway 57.
Seasons/ Hours:	Open year-round. Vehicle admission sticker required.
Length:	Small accessible caves approximately a quarter mile from the boat launch.
Precautions:	Very steep, difficult trail.
Amenities:	Boating, biking, camping, hiking, picnicking, fishing, hunting and trapping, cross-country skiing, snowmobiling, showshoeing, and sledding. Nature center and naturalist programs.
Contact	Potawatomi State Park, 3740 County Road PD, Sturgeon Bay, WI 54235. Phone: 920/746-2890. Website: http://dnr.wi.gov/topic/parks/name/ potawatomi/.

ROCK ISLAND STATE PARK
DOOR COUNTY

The Wisconsin Speleological Society surveyed seven significant Rock Island Lighthouse Caves in 1986, recording maps of their size and location about twenty feet below the top of the ridge below the Potawatomie Lighthouse, on both sides of a stone stairway leading to the shore. They extend from about ten to thirty-two feet in length in the Niagara dolomite, with entrances varying from four feet to twelve feet in height.

Somewhat surprisingly, these are unlike the littoral caves of Peninsula and Potawatomi state parks. The Rock Island Lighthouse Caves are solutional caves, hollowed through the action of glacial ice melt, springs, carbonic acid, and temperature variations—similar to those at Cherney Maribel Caves County Park. At some point, the cliff face fell away, exposing the caves and cutting their entrances. A twelve-foot high natural bridge connects two cave entrances; likely the two caves and bridge were once a single, sixty-two-foot-long cave passage.

Like the other Door County state parks, Rock Island offers excellent hiking and camping opportunities, along with a pristine swimming beach. Many campers also swim from the cobblestone shores near their campsites. The primary drawbacks are the island's remoteness and relative inaccessibility during the winter.

The Friends of Rock Island State Park offer free (donations accepted) tours of Pottawatomie Lighthouse daily from 10 a.m. to 4 p.m. from Memorial Day through Columbus Day. During tours, visitors may even climb to the lantern room.

Directions:	Take State Highway 42 to Northport at the tip of the Door County Peninsula. Take the Washington Island Ferry to Washington Island. Cross the island to the northeast side to the Rock Island ferry landing. Leave your vehicle or bike there and take the passengers-only Rock Island Ferry to Rock Island.
Seasons/ Hours:	Open year-round, 6 a.m. to 11 p.m., but the ferry runs only from Memorial Day weekend to Columbus Day weekend. Travel over the ice not recommended.
Length:	Several caves range from approximately ten to thirty-two feet in length.
Precautions:	The closest doctor is six miles away on Washington Island; the closest hospital is fifty-five miles distant in Sturgeon Bay.
Amenities:	Boating, camping, hiking, picnicking, fishing, and hunting and trapping, as well as lighthouse tours, 10 a.m. to 4 p.m., daily, from Memorial Day weekend through Columbus Day weekend.
Contact	Rock Island State Park, 1924 Indian Point Rd, Washington, WI 5424. Phone: 920/847-2235. Website: http://dnr.wi.gov/topic/parks/name/rockisland/.

WEQUIOCK FALLS COUNTY PARK
BROWN COUNTY

To the left of the falls, above, is a shallow rock shelter with tree roots growing down from the overhang.

This small gem of a county park along State Highway 57 offers a wild respite on a busy day. From the parking area follow the trail to the bridge and overlook, and then descend a rough, rocky trail to the falls. Use caution, particularly when the trail is wet. As you face the falls, gaze a bit to the left to see a shallow rock shelter, with several exposed tree roots hanging down like stalactites.

Directions:	Northeast of Green Bay, take State Highway 57 (Sturgeon Bay Road) to Van Laanen Road, and then take the first right to the park entrance.
Seasons/ Hours:	Open year-round until 8 p.m., but for the best views, plan a visit in spring or following a heavy rain.
Precautions:	Steep, rough, unmaintained trail.
Amenities:	Picnic tables, restrooms, drinking water.
Contact	Brown County Parks Department, PO Box 23600, Green Bay WI 54305; phone: 920/448-6242. Website: www.co.brown.wi.us/departments/ page_87b205fddb72/?department=260ed145263d&subdepartment= dadc284c6c54. (No line break in URL.) Park address: 3426 Bay Settlement Rd, Green Bay, WI 54311.

WILDCAT MOUNTAIN STATE PARK
VERNON COUNTY

Mountain lions probably don't roam Wildcat Mountain State Park—though a number of people swear they've seen one. And the park's Ice Cave isn't really a cave, though as you approach the sandstone overhang, it sure looks like a cave entrance. Closer investigation reveals a shallow depression in the rock, with a spring flowing over the upper edge. In the winter this small stream freezes, forming a giant icicle—and the ice cave—that lasts into June in cool years.

To reach the formation, follow the short Ice Cave Trail from the picnic area on Billings Creek, at the junction of State Highway 33 and County Highway F. Located in the unglaciated Kickapoo Valley, Wildcat Mountain also offers more challenging hiking on the two-and-a-half-mile Old Settler's Trail through the upper wooded areas of the park and on the one-and-a-third-mile Hemlock Trail, which winds upward from the Kickapoo River.

Perched on a ridge above the winding Kickapoo River, the 3,643-acre park earned its name when farmers tracked a bobcat that had killed several area sheep. They shot and killed it near the current park overlook.

Today the former lumbering region offers a wide range of outdoor activities in addition to hiking and is particularly known for its fifteen miles of horse trails, as well as canoe access to the Kickapoo River. The longest Wisconsin River tributary, the 130-mile long Kickapoo twists along the base of the park's sandstone and dolomite-capped cliffs. It snakes through the so-called Ocooch Mountains, named after a small band of

Directions:	Located southeast of Ontario and northwest of Hillsboro on State Highway 33.
Seasons/ Hours:	Open year-round, 6 a.m. to 11 p.m. Vehicle admission sticker required.
Length:	Ice Cave Trail is about one-third mile long.
Precautions:	This is an easy trail for most hikers.
Amenities:	Wildcat Mountain especially attracts canoeists and equestrians. There is an equestrian campground with two dozen campsites, hitching posts, a corral, and loading ramp. Also available: traditional camping, hiking, picnicking, toilets, fishing, hunting, and trapping. Come winter, the park features seven miles of cross-country ski trails and a two-and-a-half mile snowshoe trail. A snowmobile trail crosses a section of the park.
Contact	Wildcat Mountain State Park, E13660 State Hwy 33, P.O. Box 99, Ontario, WI 54651. Phone: 608/337-4775. Website: http://dnr.wi.gov/topic/parks/name/wildcat/.

Indians related to the Ho-Chunk called the "Ocoche," and wiped out by smallpox. The mountains are castellated bluffs, carved by wind, water, and ice over millennia.

Although the park does not offer canoe rentals, several liveries are located in Ontario and other nearby towns. All offer shuttle service to the river.

While you're in the area, you may want to visit a different type of underground attraction: the park is an easy drive from the tunnels on the Elroy-Sparta State Trail and the Omaha County Trail. Biking, however, is one activity not permitted on the trails of Wildcat Mountain State Park.

WYALUSING STATE PARK
GRANT COUNTY

Situated above the confluence of the Wisconsin and Mississippi Rivers, the area that is now Wyalusing State Park was once a neutral ground where at least fourteen Native American tribes lived or visited to trade. The park, which celebrated its centennial in 2017, takes its name from "Wyalusing" a Munsee-Delaware Indian word meaning, "home of the warrior."

When Father Jacques Marquette and Louis Joliet journeyed down the Fox and Wisconsin rivers, they reached this confluence and Native American gathering place in the summer of 1673. A few years later, French voyageurs arrived to trade various goods for furs from the Native Americans. Over the next 250 years, many different people traveled through the area—including soldiers, miners, and farmers.

The river banks and bluffs have changed little since the fourteen tribes walked these lands. They must have marveled at the area's rugged beauty the same way that visitors today are struck by its sweeping vistas, 500-foot cliffs, and quiet, wooded trails. Yet some of the park's best attractions are underground: the openings of several small caves mark the bluffs, and rock shelters guard a few of the wooded valleys.

Hiking to Treasure Cave begins at Point Lookout. The paved Bluff Trail and stairways lead you down the face of the cliff and through the keyhole—a narrow passage through a limestone outcrop. You then climb up to the cave. When you reach the top, you can head to the right and crawl through a short passage to a rock-framed window looking out on the Wisconsin River. Or you can go straight into the cave. At the back of the entrance room, a crawl tunnel leads to another room about three feet in height and large enough for perhaps a dozen people to sit snugly. Coming out of the cool, damp cave on a sunny day, people who wear glasses may be temporarily "fogged in."

Inside Big Sand Cave

Treasure Cave got its name from a legend dating to the time that Fort Crawford, located at Prairie du Chien, guarded the area. According to the story, bandits stole a quantity of gold from the fort's paymaster. Pursued by soldiers, the thieves buried the loot on a high bluff near the mouth of the Wisconsin River.

A more unusual story is associated with Big Sand Cave, which is really a shelter under a rock overhang. As this legend goes, early settlers raised hogs and let them run wild in the winter to forage for acorns in the woods. For years, however, rustlers stole many of the animals during the winter. The farmers finally discovered that two men were butchering the hogs and putting them in cold storage at Big Sand Cave until they could raft them to Prairie du Chien when the rivers opened. To reach Big Sand Cave, park at near the Paul Lawrence Interpretative Center (named for the park's first superintendent) and hike the trail about a half mile east. Continue along the Little Sand Cave Loop to reach a smaller cave beneath a waterfall.

Pictured Rock Cave is a forty-foot-wide shelter, cut underneath a small waterfall that feeds a stream at the base of the shelter. To get there, take the Sugar Maple Nature Trail off of the Homestead Picnic Area and watch for the short side trail that leads to the cave. The distance from the picnic area parking lot to Pictured Rock Cave is less than a

Looking out of Big Sand Cave

half mile. Hike or showshoe to Pictured Rock Cave and Little Sand Cave in winter to see the frozen waterfalls.

You can see rock outcrops and bluff faces along other park trails, although some trails were destroyed and later reconfigured and reconstructed following torrential rains in 2007. Today approximately twenty miles of trails wend through the rocky confluence region of the Wisconsin and Mississippi Rivers.

Other developments include the Lawrence L. Huser Astronomy Center, which opened in 2003. Named for a longtime park ranger, the center and observatory are located about a hundred yards down a gravel path past the park office. A local nonprofit, the StarSplitters Astronomy Club (http://www.starsplitters.org/), has partnered with the park to offer programs on selected Saturday nights from May through October. When the skies are clear, these presentations include viewing planets, constellations, and more.

Like other Wisconsin state parks, Wyalusing has an active Friends group, a nonprofit committed to enhancing the interpretative and recreational opportunities of the park. The Friends of Wyalusing State Park (http://www.wyalusingfriends.org/p/ the-friends-of-wyalusing.html) annually provides volunteer time and funds to support such projects as park signage, events calendar, and various restoration projects.

When you've finished climbing and searching for caves, Wyalusing offers many other activities—such as swimming, boating, or just relaxing by a campfire. Two sites operated by the Wisconsin Historical Society are also nearby: Villa Louis in Prairie du Chien was the elegant mansion once owned by the state's first millionaire, and Stonefield Village near Cassville recreates an 1890s agricultural community.

Directions:	Take U.S. 18 south from Prairie du Chien; turn right on County Highway C to County Highway X. Turn right on X and follow it to the park.
Seasons/ Hours:	Open year-round, 6 a.m. to 11 p.m. Vehicle admission sticker required.
Length:	Caves are all small; and the length of the trails to reach them and return varies from less than a mile to close to two miles.
Precautions:	Trails range in difficulty; some are steep and can be slick when wet or covered with leaves or ice. Bring a flashlight to explore Treasure Cave.
Amenities:	Canoe and kayak rental available in seasonal concession stand. Biking, hiking, boating, camping, canoeing, fishing, picnicking, nature center, toilets, hunting and trapping, snowshoeing, and cross-country skiing.
Contact	Wyalusing State Park, 13081 State Park Ln., Bagley, WI 53801. Phone: 608/996-2261. Website: http://dnr.wi.gov/topic/parks/name/wyalusing/.

Little Sand Cave
(Photos: Connie Frazier)

IOWA CAVES

Iowa has perhaps as many caves as Wisconsin, and several are within an hour's drive of Wisconsin's border and the Mississippi River. Each of the sites in this section offers one or more unique features not readily available in Wisconsin caves. You may want to see the unusual flower-like formations or clear lake in Crystal Lake Cave, experience the variety of caving opportunities at Maquoketa Caves State Park, or explore Spook Cave by boat. Extending your cave explorations a bit beyond Wisconsin's borders can provide a broader view of caves in general, as well as a glimpse of several unusual features.

CRYSTAL LAKE CAVE
DUBUQUE COUNTY, IOWA

Miners hoping to find a vein of lead ore found instead Crystal Lake Cave in 1868. James Rice and his crew sank a shaft forty feet through the limestone, and Rice, coming on a crevice, explored 700 feet of a natural passage, finally reaching a large cave system. The first adventurous visitors to the then-called Rice's Cave entered via a bucket lowered by rope into a shaft.

What they saw was part of the same mineral wonderland you can see today, albeit with more layers of mud and rock fragments on the floor. The cave system, which extends for several miles, lies seventy-five to 100 feet underneath the rolling hills; some passages remain inaccessible to most visitors. But what is accessible is breathtaking.

Developed and officially opened to the public in 1932, Crystal Lake Cave has preserved many beautiful formations, including stalactites, stalagmites, helectites, and several rare anthodites, or cave flowers. These white clusters somewhat resemble a dahlia, with narrow petals radiating from the center. They actually are crystals of aragonite, a mineral made up of calcium carbonate and in some ways similar to calcite.

Crystal Lake Cave aragonite formations
(Photo: Crystal Lake Cave)

Today you enter nature's showroom by descending twenty-eight concrete steps. (This stairway is steep, but it represents a considerable improvement over a rope and bucket!) The walkway at the base of the stairway is also paved, leading you through the passages as surely as Dorothy's yellow brick road.

Your Emerald City, however, is Crystal Lake. Lying at the end of a long passage, the lake extends twenty-eight feet into the main passage ahead of you. It is three to four feet wide and two-and-a-half feet deep. But its real attraction hangs overhead and on the glassy surface where the reflections of a multitude of stalactites shimmer in the lamplight.

All the rooms that break up the narrow passageways seem relatively small; however, couples have held marriage ceremonies in the Chapel Room. And the undeveloped portion of the cave includes two large rooms, including the Flat Room, which extends ninety feet through the limestone. Many of the rooms and shoulder-brushing passages are festooned with soda straws and other stalactites and furnished with stalagmites.

Named years ago, the wonderful formations really look like their names. You can readily see the Tyrannosaurus Rex, for example, not to mention all the animals of Noah's Ark, in Imagination Alley. And, the Swiss cottage roof with its overhanging straw or icicles belongs in a stage version of Heidi. The cave offers a kind of field of dreams, where every room stirs a memory—here a petrified forest, there a Disney cartoon character, and over there, perhaps, an evocative movie hero from childhood.

Breaking the dream, an earthenware jug rests in a small niche in the wall, a leftover from the nineteenth century. And a sign proclaims, "$50 fine for breaking or destroying crystals." You're glad to see this effort at cave conservation but wish the intrusive reminder was unnecessary.

Directions:	Located five miles south of Dubuque, left off of U.S. 52. Watch for signs.
Seasons/ Hours:	Open daily from 9 a.m. to 6 p.m. from Memorial Day to mid-August. See website or call for reduced spring and fall hours, from early May through October. Fee. Last tour leaves one hour before closing. Phone to learn more about the one-and-a-half hour wild cave tour.
Length:	Approximately three quarters of a mile; tour lasts forty-five minutes.
Precautions:	Light jacket recommended; temperature is fifty degrees. Lowest passage measures five feet, three inches in height.
Amenities:	Picnicking, shelters, restrooms, gem-mining sluice for kids.
Contact	Crystal Lake Cave, 6684 Crystal Lake Cave Dr., Dubuque, IA 52003. Phone: 319/556-6451. Website: www.crystallakecave.com.

Too soon, you reach Tall Man's Misery, the five-foot-three-inch-high final passage. The forty-five minute tour seemed like a quarter of an hour. You exit by climbing another set of steps and walk outside perhaps 200 feet south of the entrance.

After a picnic on the Crystal Lake Cave grounds, you may want to check out the nearby Mines of Spain State Recreation Area (http://www.minesofspain.org/). Though not offering any opportunities to venture underground, it honors the first European to mine the area. Julien Dubuque received a land grant from the governor of Spain in New Orleans in 1796. The grant gave Dubuque the right to work the area, to be called "Mines of Spain." The recreation area features the 1897 Julien Dubuque Monument (an interpretative center), picnicking, and twenty-one miles of hiking trails. To reach the Mines of Spain, drive north toward Dubuque on U.S. 52 from Crystal Lake Cave and watch for signs.

MAQUOKETA CAVES STATE PARK
JACKSON COUNTY, IOWA

The only thing wrong with Maquoketa Caves State Park is that it's in Iowa, and not Wisconsin. With more than a dozen caves of varying lengths—and widths—Maquoketa Caves State Park offers great caving for experienced and inexperienced cavers alike. If you have explored Wisconsin's commercial caves and feel ready for more—but not for a truly difficult crawl—you may want to visit Maquoketa. It offers an introduction to the exploration of undeveloped caves.

Interpreters provide guided tours and facilitate the White Nose Syndrome (WNS) Awareness Program. Attendance at this short program is required for those who plan to enter the caves.

Dancehall Cave, the largest in the park, extends more than 1,000 feet. Partly developed by the Civilian Conservation Corps and Works Progress Administration in the 1930s, Dancehall has a paved walkway and lighting system. The lights, however, are interspersed relatively far apart; a flashlight can help illumine your path and prevent slips, especially if you have small children in your group. Occasionally, there are puddles on the winding walkway, and a stream flows on either side. The cave itself is very broad, as much as twenty feet wide in places, and has three easily accessible entrances. The ceiling height ranges from approximately four to forty feet, and you can stand up in it except near the entrances.

The other caves, all smaller, are generally located on a line of limestone bluffs and vary greatly in size and shape. You can stand up in several—for example, standing and looking out of Twin Arch Cave, you can see one of the entrances to Dancehall. On the other hand, Dug Out Cave is only accessible by crawling; and some previous caving experience is useful to fully explore Wye Cave. Maps of some of the caves are posted near the first parking area. If you want to explore the undeveloped caves, be sure to wear a long-sleeved shirt—and bring a complete change of clothing. After all, getting muddy is part of the fun!

Curious about the complete list of caves? Here it is:

- Barbell Cave
- Dancehall Cave
- Dug Out Cave
- Hernando's Hideaway
- Ice Cave
- Match Cave
- Rainy Day Cave
- Shinbone Cave
- Twin Arch Cave
- Up-N-Down Cave
- Wide Mouth Cave
- Window Cave

A six-mile system of trails links the caves, including wooden walkways and stairways that provide access to cave entrances located on steep hillsides. Occasional benches provide a place to rest and appreciate views of the wooded valley and Raccoon Creek. In addition to the caves, Maquoketa offers two other natural features not to be missed: a fifty-foot natural bridge spanning the creek and a seventeen-ton balanced rock. One trail passes a restored prairie, an experimental oak savanna restoration, and a wildlife food plot.

If you visit Maquoketa on a summer weekend, you will want to see the excellent exhibits in the interpretative center, located near the park entrance. Displays on the cave formations, geology, early Native American culture, and park history help you see the area's natural wonders through a long lens. White settlers discovered the caves in 1834, after two hunters tracked a deer into Dancehall Cave; yet Native Americans had known about the caves for many years. There's also a video tour for people unable to hike to the caves; it's available on summer weekends and at other times by arrangement with the park office.

When they were rediscovered by the settlers, the caves contained many stalactites and stalagmites, which vandals and souvenir hunters have destroyed. The caves still contain some dripstone and flowstone, along with draperies and a few soda straws. But it will be many years before Maquoketa visitors again find sizable stalactites and stalagmites.

Directions:	Take U.S. 61 south from Dubuque. As you near Maquoketa, watch for signs and turn right on State Highway 428. Drive time from Dubuque is about a half hour.
Seasons/ Hours:	Park is open year-round. Friends of Maquoketa Caves Concession is open April 22 through October 15; Friends volunteers serve as hosts at the interpretative center on Saturdays, Sundays and Memorial Day, Labor Day and the Fourth of July; 9 a.m. to 5 p.m. Free (fee for camping).
Length:	Dancehall Cave is more than 1,000 feet long, but the other caves are much smaller. Allow two to four hours to explore several caves and hike some of the trails, or a full day to thoroughly look around the park.
Precautions:	Definitely bring a light source, wear appropriate clothing, and bring a change of clothes if you plan to explore the smaller caves. No rappelling or rock climbing allowed.
Amenities:	Camping, picnicking, restrooms, hiking, biking, and an interpretative center. The campground will be closed for renovation from April through August 2018. The town of Maquoketa is seven miles from the park and offers accommodations and a variety of restaurants.
Contact	Maquoketa Caves State Park, 10970 98th St., Maquoketa, IA 52060. Phone: 319/652-5833. Website: http://www.iowadnr.gov/Places-to-Go/State-Parks/Iowa-State-Parks/ParkDetails/ParkID/610127.

SPOOK CAVE AND CAMPGROUND
CLAYTON COUNTY, IOWA

There are probably no ghosts living in Spook Cave. But a boat tour of this underworld may leave you wondering whether any otherworldly creatures abide here. Named for the eerie noises that once emanated from a small hole at the base of a bluff near the old mill town of Beulah, Iowa, Spook Cave follows a creek for at least a half mile underground. The creek eventually exits the bluff through another hole in its side, tumbling down a waterfall to a fast-moving stream below.

Spook Cave's developer, Gerald Mielke, grew up on a farm two miles away and was curious about the strange noises coming from the hill. After serving in World War II, Mielke helped develop several commercial caves in southern Minnesota and in 1953 acquired a ninety-nine-year lease on a forty-acre hill property that he guessed contained a cave. Mielke blasted a hole sixty feet into the hill and discovered Spook Cave. Soon he created another tunnel into the cave, providing access to the first large room that visitors now encounter. Finally, Mielke enlarged the hole from which the unusual sounds issued, constructing the waterway entrance still in use today.

Then the real work of cave development began. Mielke and his helpers removed rocks from the cave floor, dredged out sediment, and created a small pond just outside the waterway entrance. The pond raised the level of the stream enough to allow custom-built aluminum boats to penetrate almost 1,000 feet into Spook Cave. Mielke opened his underground wilderness to visitors in 1955.

Current owners Mary Fitch and Jim and Bonnie Dougherty have continued to develop the property and conserve the cave's treasures, allowing the Iowa Karst Survey to map new areas of the stream cave and explore sections that are completely underwater, or sumped. The Iowa Department of Natural Resources has cleaned the sinkholes above Spook Cave, and tour guides ask that you not touch the formations, explaining that the oil from your hands can retard the slow growth of stalactites, stalagmites, and other speleothems.

Thanks to the conservation efforts and Spook Cave's relatively recent discovery, it remains pristinely natural, thanks to continuous maintenance activities. Cavers and guides periodically clean the passages and dredge by hand the sediment that still collects on the creek bottom.

Spook Cave contains stalactites throughout its main passage, growing from the ceiling and overhangs in several domes. A number of these vertical shafts punctuate the main passage; the tallest of these rises forty feet above the stream. Despite the presence of the creek running over the cave floor, you still can see many stalagmites, as well as stalactites, flowstone, and draperies. Although no spooks appear peeking around columns or from behind the curtains, you still wonder what may lurk in the shadows and the incompletely explored depths.

Floating through this fragile wonderland, you lose awareness of time and direction. The aboveground world seems centuries distant. When you finally emerge into the warm sunshine, you may want to stroll about the campground to regain you land legs. The property offers picnicking, swimming, and plenty of other activities.

There's even a waterfall and a replica of an old mill with a twelve-foot waterwheel weighing in at about 3,000 pounds. Its inspiration, Shellhammer Mill, was a grist mill located a bit further downstream on Bloody Run Creek. Gerald Mielke constructed the limestone-faced replica in 1957. That same year he brought two one-room schoolhouses to the property, joining them into a T-shape, and converting the combined schoolhouses into the cave's office. Today, the Spook Cave Lodge offers a photographic history of the cave's development, snacks, and souvenirs.

Directions:	Located ten miles west of Prairie du Chien, Wisconsin, on U.S. 18 and 52. Turn right on Spook Cave Road.
Seasons/ Hours:	Open daily, 9 a.m. to 5:30 p.m., from May 1 through October. Fee.
Length:	The forty-minute boat tour winds through nearly 1,000 feet of the cave's main passage.
Precautions:	Light jacket recommended; cave temperature is forty-seven degrees year-round.
Amenities:	Camping, cabin rental, restrooms, picnicking, playgrounds, sand volleyball, hiking, biking, swimming, kayaking, paddle boating, stocked trout stream, hiking, and playground.
Contact	Spook Cave and Campground, 13299 Spook Cave Rd., McGregor, IA 53157. Phone: 319/873-2144. Website: http://spookcave.com/.

This rusting capsule once ferried miners up the shaft at the Bevans Mine.

SECTION TWO

MINES

VILLAGE OF POTOSI

One of Wisconsin's early mining communities, Potosi was settled in 1829 after lead ore was found near St. John Mine. Named for the silver mining city of "Potosi" in Bolivia, South America, the village began as three separate settlements and developed along the steep walls of the narrow valley, incorporating in 1841. Located on the Grant River feeding into the Mississippi, Potosi quickly became a leading shipping port for lead ore and a supplier for inland miners. Potosi was one of the largest communities in the Wisconsin Territory, but its early boom was short-lived: by the late 1840s, its port filled with river silt, no longer accommodating large vessels, and the promise of gold in California drew many area miners further west. However, Potosi's mining industry was revived in the later half of the 19th century when zinc, a by-product of lead mining, was produced. The Potosi Brewery, built by Gabriel Hall in 1855, remained an important industry for over a hundred years.

Erected 1996

Several Wisconsin State Historical markers document mines and mining history.

Given the importance of mining in Wisconsin's development, it's amazing that more hasn't been written about the hundreds of lead, zinc, iron, and copper operations that once dotted the state's landscape. Although you may find little mention of mining attractions in popular travel articles, reminders of the industry still exist and are as tangible as the ruins of a shaft house or a chunk of lead ore, heavy in your hand.

Where do you find these remnants and relics? While many old mines lay long buried under lands as varied as state parks and city streets, a few have been given new life and reopened to visitors. In some cases, efforts by towns and historical societies have combined to preserve a mine; in other cases, private enterprise has invested the resources needed to maintain an old tunnel.

Cleaned, and sometimes with new supports, several of the old passages are as passable today as they were a century or more ago. The shafts that once provided entry and exit for miners and ore now provide ventilation for tour groups. Yet little else has changed.

Descending into one of these old tunnels is like meeting an ancestor. You can see where one miner dug a small exploratory side tunnel off the main passage and the spot where another hammered out a small hole for blasting powder. There's a pile of ore on the floor just waiting to be loaded into a cart and drawn to the surface. And there's a clear vein or ore waiting to be dug out. Rounding a corner in the tunnel, you wouldn't be at all surprised to meet an old-time miner, dressed in tall boots, dusty clothes, and a battered leather hat. Maybe he's carrying a pick in one hand and a candle in the other. You half expect this apparition to hand you the pick and motion for you to start work.

Shaking your head, you come back to the present in time to hear the guide explain that there was an accident near this spot in the mine. A rockfall killed a miner and ended the excavation in this direction. In other parts of the mine, you may find a stream, scattered mining tools, or even ore cart rails.

The artifacts and sensations involved in entering this underworld combine to provide a deeply felt experience. Although entering an old mine tunnel is somewhat similar to visiting an aboveground, living history museum, going underground often provokes more profound feelings, you have literally entered a time tunnel. You may wonder about the details of the miners' lives, the lives of your great-grandparents, and even reincarnation. Who knows? When you're underground, mysteries abound.

There are only two opportunities to explore old underground mines in Wisconsin, both in the southwest corner of the state. But you can still view mining remnants aboveground at many locales. For example, the Flambeau Mine, which ceased its copper and gold mining operations in 1999, has backfilled its pit and created a five-mile network of trails on the 150-acre site on State Highway 27 near Ladysmith. (Websites: https://ruskcountywi.com/reclaimed-flambeau-mine-nature-trails and https://dnr.wi.gov/topic/Mines/Flambeau.html.)

Who knows? The jury is still out on whether there will ever be a new, underground mine in Wisconsin.

Following significant and long-running controversy about a proposed, underground copper and zinc mine near Crandon, the U.S. Supreme Court decided in 2002 that Indian nations could set their own, environmental restrictions. The decision marked the end of the proposal's economic viability, and in 2003, the Mole Lake Ojibwe and Forest County Potawatomi purchased the mine site.

In 2015, Gogebic Taconite decided that its proposal to mine iron near the Menominee River along the Wisconsin-Michigan border was unfeasible due to federal and state environment laws. Lawmakers, however, at both the state and federal levels are working to weaken applicable laws.

Governor Scott Walker signed a measure in 2017 clearing the way for mining copper and gold in Wisconsin, despite opposition from environmental opponents. The governor repealed a law that essentially prevented companies from extracting minerals besides iron because of pollution concerns.

Controversy also swirls about the growth and expansion of the state's sand mines and quarries, including, for example, the Bay Silica Company, which operates a mine along the Mississippi River between Maiden Rock and Bay City. Wisconsin sand is being shipped by rail for use in hydraulic fracturing operations at oil wells. There is some evidence that the process can trigger earthquakes and pose other environmental hazards near the wells. As of 2016 there were more than ninety active industrial sand facilities across the state, many in West Central Wisconsin.

These sites are generally inaccessible, as are most of the state's former iron mining sites. As only one example, few people today have heard of the Cahoon Mine, an iron mine that operated before and during World War I near Baraboo.

Iron mining also occurred south of Mayville in Dodge County from the 1840s to the 1920s. Wisconsin's Iron Ridge here is actually part of a several-mile-long segment of the Niagara Escarpment containing iron deposits. You can see the ridge by driving from Beaver Dam west on State Highway 33 to State Highway 67. Turn south on State Highway 67. You can see a segment of the Niagara Escarpment on your left (east);

mining activity centered on this ridge from about a half mile to two miles south of State Highway 33.

The Neda Iron Mine operated on this ridge until about 1915. Today owned by the University of Wisconsin-Milwaukee, the mine is a large bat hibernacula, especially for little brown bats, as well as northern long-eared bats, eastern pipistrelle bats, and big brown bats. The university's College of Letters and science Neda Mine Field Station works with the Wisconsin Department of Natural Resources to protect the hibernacula and monitor these populations. See: http://uwm.edu/field-station/about/natural-areas/neda-mine.

Another former iron mine site is more accessible. The Jackson County Iron Mine has been restored into a popular park, its water-filled pit now a major scuba diving destination.

For a closer look at underground iron mining, you can explore the Iron Mountain Iron Mine, located just over the Wisconsin border in Michigan. And while you're in the Upper Peninsula, you also may want to visit one or more of the several old copper mines that now offer public tours. Included here are descriptions of several of Michigan's guided mine tours.

In comparison, the early lead and zinc mines of Southwest Wisconsin appear small and primitive, yet they brought an influx of people and wealth to the region and helped pave the way for statehood. The opportunity to visit two of these old mines today represents a type of educational wealth hard to duplicate, even with video and virtual reality technology. They offer a literal time tunnel to the past.

WISCONSIN LEAD, ZINC, COPPER, AND IRON MINE SITES

When Wisconsinites think about lead mining in the state, they may reflect on the days when the lead rush opened Southwest Wisconsin to settlement. The mines that are open today to visitors focus primarily on this nineteenth-century history. The low, hand-dug tunnels and the hand tools give testimony to the huge individual effort that went into this period of the state's growth.

Though hard to believe, lead and zinc mining continued here to some degree into the 1970s. more than three hundred mines existed in Southwest Wisconsin over the years; thirty were still operating in 1952, employing about seven hundred miners. By the mid 1970s, only two remained—the Eagle Picher in Shullsburg and the Piggy Sow near Mineral Point; and by 1980, they, too, had closed.

This mining life remains accessible today through historic sites and museums. Going underground into these early mines can provide a small sense of day-to-day life in the mining region of Wisconsin Territory. It was a rough life—full of hard physical labor, noise, dirt, and danger.

Now we may wonder, "How did they do that?" Exploring these sites can provide some answers. And a better understanding of the miners' experience can enlarge our perspective, perhaps even enabling us to meet our own times and challenges with an equal amount of energy and perseverance.

We begin this exploration in Shullsburg in the heart of the lead region. The city-operated Badger Mine is actually a section of a five-mile system of old tunnels running beneath the modern-day town. Jesse Shull, founder of Shullsburg, established his Badger Lot Diggings in the late 1820s on a spot where he had seen Native Americans digging for lead. Today, you can enter his mine via a spiral stairway built into the original shaft. Besides providing a first-hand experience of early lead mining, the site offers an extensive museum, containing early agricultural, household, medical, and industrial artifacts, as well as mining relics.

The Mining Museum and the Bevans Mine in Platteville offer a similar combination; in fact, it would be easy to spend half a day poking around the various exhibits and touring the mine. The Bevans Mine dates from 1845, when Lorenzo Bevans and fifteen employees dug two million pounds of lead from the mine in a single year. Today the site also depicts many processes associated with zinc mining. Weather permitting, a highlight of the tour is a ride in an narrow gauge rail car behind a 1931 locomotive that runs to a hoist house where you can see how zinc ore was sorted.

A twenty-minute drive to the northeast brings you to Mineral Point and the site of the Merry Christmas Mine, a zinc mine begun by Isaac Suthers in 1905. Although you can no longer enter this mine, you can hike along two self-guided trails that point out several mine ruins. You also can walk across the street and tour Pendarvis, a state historic site featuring early Cornish homes and depicting life in the early mining community.

Badger Mine and Museum
Lafayette County

Where do you expect to find an abandoned mine? There may be few more unlikely places than in the middle of a city park in Shullsburg. Surrounded by a swimming pool, tennis courts, a ball field, and playground equipment, the Badger Mine area offers enough activities to keep the whole family entertained for half a day or more. The city opens and operates this attraction from Memorial Day through Labor Day.

The plain, single-floor, russet-stained wooden building suits its park surroundings. Once inside, its appearance changes completely. You might be in an old warehouse, barn, or depot, considering the collection of material culture from generations gone by.

Constructed above the mine shaft, the building houses an entryway and museum.

Looking around, you might notice an old hotel sign riddled with holes. The story is that members of Al Capone's gang robbed the Shullsburg bank in 1925. When the gang members were making their getaway, a man stuck his head out a window on the hotel's second floor to see what was going on. One of the robbers told him to get back inside, firing several warning shots into the sign. The outlaws got away with $20,000. Later they were arrested—and then acquitted due to lack of evidence. The money was never found.

The museum offers exhibits on an amazing range of eras and artifacts. There's an agricultural implements section, a blacksmith shop, a carpenter shop, a military room, and a carriage once used by Shullsburg's first veterinarian, along with two horse-drawn sleds.

Flanked by a drugstore and tobacconist, a general store displays a hodgepodge of useful goods—wire-rimmed sunglasses, coffee, thread, buttons, needles and other sewing notions. Loyal Wisconsinites also will be interested in the display of cheese cutters, boxes, and other early cheese industry items.

There's a furnished turn-of-the-century kitchen and child's bedroom, as well as a parlor outfitted with a square, solid oak piano built in New York City in 1854. The piano was shipped by boat to New Orleans and then up the Mississippi River to Galena. From there, it traveled by wagon to arrive in Shullsburg several months later.

One of the most intriguing exhibits is a re-creation of the first woman physician in the area, Mary Peebles Gratiot, who practiced from 1871 to 1904. The exhibit contains early dental tools, wheelchairs, a hospital bed, and an x-ray machine.

Your circuit of the museum ends at the early mining exhibits, which feature such artifacts as ore samples, tools, leather hard hats, three-level lunch pails (for coffee, hot pasty, and dessert), and stick-in-tommies—candles on metal hooks that could be attached to the front of a hat or, more often, stuck in the wall of a mine. Candle-making was a daily chore in Wisconsin's early mining days. There are also examples of sunshine lamps, small oil lamps that eventually replaced the candles.

A working replica of Eagle Pitcher Mine, located in Galena, Illinois, is impossible to ignore. Crafted by Arnold Fox (a Platteville native born in 1924), the seven-foot replica showcases the steps involved in late nineteenth-century mine operations.

Jess Shull, founder of Shullsburg, established the then-called Badger Lot Diggings where he had seen Native Americans digging for lead. Shull had explored the region as early as 1818 for the Hudson's Bay Fur Company and began his mine about 1827.

To enter his mine today, you bravely descend a steep, spiral stairway built into the original shaft. Every few steps, you make a sharp right-angle turn until you finally reach the bottom of the fifty-two-step stairs. In the early days of Shull's mine, teenage boys too young for the dangerous work of the mine operated a windlass at the top of the shaft, hauling a large bucket that carried men, equipment, and ore.

Badger Mine is actually a section of a five-mile system of tunnels that runs underneath modern-day Shullsburg. While the location of most of the main tunnels is known, many side tunnels have not yet been completely re-explored and mapped.

Badger Mine tour

The main drift—or horizontal passage along a mineral vein—is hardly more than five feet high in places, requiring a bit of stooping and bending. Overhead, stalactites have begun to form though the action of water dripping through the limestone.

A small lead vein is visible in the wall, and numerous, tiny side tunnels branch off the main passage. Although the prospect of exploring them may be tempting, one could get lost in the unmapped passages. Loose rock fills some of the side tunnels, since the early miners often found it easier to shovel debris into tunnels no longer in use than to carry it to the surface. Also appearing on the walls of the main passage are the initials of several miners, burned into the rock with a candle.

Stuck high on one wall, a dog's skull peers down into the main passage. The legend is that one miner often took his dog with him into the mine. One day when the miners blasted, they forgot to get the dog out and it was crushed. There is a curse attached to this legend: If anyone takes the skull down, supposedly the mine will collapse.

Badger Mine contains evidence of blasting, and you still can see cylindrical holes in the walls, made to hold blasting powder. Sometimes, when the last miner came up the shaft just before blasting, he dropped a hot coal on a line of blasting powder that served as a fuse—and then got to the surface as quickly as possible.

Once, the miners tunneled into a natural cavern, and in another instance, they dug a low, narrow channel alongside a fast-moving underground stream. You can see the stream; however, crawling into this passage is prohibited. The passage continues almost to a spring at the head of the stream.

Directions:	Take State Highway 11 to Shullsburg; turn south on County Highway O and then left on West Estey Street. The Badger Mine and Museum will be on your left.
Seasons/ Hours:	Open 11:30 a.m. to 4 p.m. daily from Memorial Day through Labor Day. Fee.
Length:	Tour winds about a half mile within the five miles of tunnels existing fifty-plus feet beneath Shullsburg. Allow two hours for a complete tour, including the museum.
Precautions:	Access is via a steep, spiral staircase. Light sweater or jacket recommended; cave temperature is about fifty degrees.
Amenities:	Adjacent Badger Park contains picnic tables, grills, toilets, playground equipment, baseball field, tennis courts, and swimming pool. Miner Park on Water Street honors eight miners who were killed in Wisconsin's worst mining disaster on February 9, 1943.
Contact	(In season only), Badger Mine and Museum, 279 W. Estey St., Shullsburg, WI 535586. Phone: 608/965-4860. Website: http://badgermineandmuseum.com/.

As the mine lengthened, a second shaft was eventually added, and a narrow-gauge rail system enabled the miners to take ore out from the newer shaft. You still can see rail car tracks in the main passage.

Long after the lead era, zinc was mined here for a short time in the early 1900s, and other Shullsburg zinc mines kept going for years after this one closed. In fact, the last southwestern Wisconsin mine ceased operations in Shullsburg in 1979. Perhaps it is fitting that the town that sprung from one of the region's first mines also harbored the last mine.

BADGER HUT VS. BADGER HOLE

Historians need to be precise and there has been some confusion over the years between the terms "badger hut" and "badger hole." For example, the "Badger Hut Trail" in Potosi probably never contained badger huts.

Tracey Lee Roberts, University of Wisconsin-Platteville, has researched the question. She writes:

The terms Badger Hut and Badger Hole refer to spaces used as housing in Southwest Wisconsin and Northwest Illinois in the early lead mining days from about 1825 to 1860. The early miners from the southern regions of Missouri and Tennessee talked about abodes known locally as badger holes; these were subterranean dwellings. These badger holes were made from sucker holes, or shallow diggings where lead was explored for and perhaps not found. Going into an already dug hole, miners would open it up to a ten-by-twelve-foot area and prop up the walls of the shallow hole with sapling poles. For a roof, the pit could be covered with downed timbers and then a couple of feet of earth and sod. According to John H. Rountree, one of the first settlers of Platteville, he spent his first winter in a sod hut. While there are no longer any remains of badger holes used as human shelter, on the Merry Christmas Mine Hill in Mineral Point, you can walk the path and encounter numerous shallow abandoned mine diggings. Others could have been used as badger holes.

In Potosi, there is an old lead mine hill with shallow pits circled by rough limestone blocks. The National Register of Historic Places was called in to study these two pits in 1986. Legend had it that these were homes for miners. Local historians wanted to verify that these

Photo of a badger hut displayed in the Badger Mine and Museum, Shullsburg

remnants were authentic and historically important. In the end, the report listed the location as the "Potosi Badger Huts Site". Upon studying this report and the actual site, I think that at best these could be remains of "badger holes", the kind I just discussed. These holes are nothing like the structures we call "badger huts."

A badger hut is a limestone, sod-covered building used to shelter early lead miners. They are generally built into a hillside or hillock and use an arched construction of undressed limestone blocks. They are roughly eleven to twelve feet long and eight to nine feet wide with a seven-foot ceiling at the apex of the arch. They are found very near old lead mines and very close to a creek or river. They are windowless and have a vent hole in the back of the roof. They are generally on private property so it is not possible to go into one. There is a good example of a badger hut that one can see from the road in winter and spring at the corner of Furlong Road near Birkbeck Road in Jo Daviess County, Illinois.

When Moses M. Strong, a lawyer and surveyor from Vermont, came to Mineral Point, in 1836, he found '".. many of the prospectors and miners living like 'badgers' in dugouts, in the side of the hills or in crude stone and clay huts." This is when Wisconsin first became known as the "Badger State."

BEVANS MINE
GRANT COUNTY

In 1845, Lorenzo Bevans and fifteen employees took two million pounds of lead from the mine that bears his name and still runs beneath the city of Platteville. One year and two million pounds was all he needed. After striking it rich, Bevans sold his mine in 1846.

Walking into the former Bevans Lead Mine on a summer day more than 170 years later is like entering a London fog. When the temperature outside rises, a dim haze forms belowground, almost as thick as the London mists. Sherlock would feel at home here, hunting criminals in its damp darkness.

You descend about fifty feet into the shallow mine via several flights and a total of ninety cement steps. You hear water dripping somewhere and note that flowstone and stalactites have begun to form on the ceiling. This mine is evolving into a cave.

Before entering the main tunnel, you don a hardhat and heft a chunk of galena (lead ore) and of sphalerite (zinc ore) just to get a feel for what the early miners had to deal with. Even though you expected it, the ore is surprisingly heavy to your inexperienced hands.

Manikins depict early lead mining in a Platteville tunnel

Entering the main tunnel, you learn what it was like to be a lead miner. You imagine yourself working on your back and your belly, using a stubby-handled pick and shovel in one of the short side tunnels to follow a small vein in the cramped space. Even though the rock in this mine is relatively soft, and mining would have been comparatively easy, the job is unpleasant at best—and dangerous at worst.

Standing in the protected present, you try to envision the low light and other working conditions of 1845. You can almost hear the pounding and prying of fifteen men working in these tunnels. No wonder that Bevans sold out after only a year. And, it's comforting to learn that there are three openings to the surface in this mine, three routes for you to escape out of and three ways to get air in.

Although Bevans mined lead exclusively, his mine today also educates about the somewhat different processes involved in zinc mining, since several zinc mines once operated in and around Platteville. For instance, one stop on the tour depicts an underground area where the miners completed the initial sorting of zinc ore. Their aim was to avoid carrying to the surface more weight than necessary.

One big difference between the lead mines and the zinc mines that followed them, beginning in the 1860s, was that the zinc mines were generally much deeper, often beneath the water table. Miners sometimes worked with water at their feet and the constant noise of a pump carrying water out of the mine.

As part of the depiction of zinc mining, a tool bench stands idle in a wider spot in the main tunnel. Equipment used in zinc mining was considerably more extensive and complex than that used in lead mining, and minor repairs to equipment were made underground.

Not far from the base of the entrance stairway a torpedo-like, man-sized cylinder fairly resembles the capsule that carried the trapped thirty-three Chilean miners half a mile to the surface in 2010. Roughly one hundred years ago, this rusting cylinder served the same purpose, ferrying miners up the shaft in safety.

Once you leave the tunnel and ascend all those steps you climbed down earlier, the zinc mining tour continues above ground. Weather permitting, you can ride a narrow-gauge rail car behind a 1931 mine locomotive, completing a small circuit behind the museum. Beginning in the 1920s, gasoline engines like this one were used in area mines, until being prohibited in the 1950s because of the carbon monoxide they spewed.

You ride to the a replica of a headframe, or hoist house, constructed over one of the original shafts of the Bevans Mine. Zinc ore was sorted in the hoist house, which also sometimes served as the miners' break room and contained a wood stove.

From the hoist house, you head for the Mining Museum, which features additional exhibits of minerals, dioramas, photographs, mining tools, and mining operations. Permanent exhibits describe lead and zinc mining, in addition to "African American Lead Miners in Wisconsin."

Owned by the city of Platteville, the museum is located in a former school, built in 1857 on the mine site. In 1972 the museum used test drilling to locate the mine, cleared it, and then opened it to the public four years later.

Adjacent to the Mining Museum, the Rollo Jamison Museum displays the collections of this lifelong collector, who began picking up arrowheads as a boy on his family farm in Beetown. Born in 1899, Jamison accumulated a diverse collection of high-quality furniture, tools, musical instruments, militaria, and other objects.

Located in Platteville's first high school constructed in 1905, the Rollo Jamison Museum, like the Mining Museum, is administered by the City of Platteville Museum Department under the direction of the museum board and city council.

Directions:	Take U.S. 151 south from Madison. In Platteville, turn right on Virgin Avenue (several blocks before State Highway 80/81). The museums are located on the corner of Virgin Avenue and Main Street.
Seasons/ Hours:	Both the Mining Museum and the Rollo Jamison Museum are open from 9 a.m. to 4 p.m. daily, from May through October. Group tours of the mine and headframe are scheduled by appointment year-round. Fee.
Length:	The mine extends about a quarter mile underneath the museum grounds. Allow about one and a half hours for a complete tour of both museums and the train ride to the hoist house.
Precautions:	There are ninety steps into the mine, which has a year-round temperature of about fifty degrees.
Amenities:	Gift shop, restrooms. Museums are located in downtown Platteville, which offers a variety of restaurants and other attractions, including the University of Wisconsin-Platteville campus.
Contact:	City of Platteville Museum Department, 405 E. Main St., P.O. Box 780, Platteville, WI 53818. Phone: 608/348-3301. Website: http://mining.jamison.museum. To read about the memories of miners, see: http://mining.jamison.museum/miners-recall-bygone-era.

BRITISH HOLLOW SMELTING FURNACE
GRANT COUNTY

The last of its kind in the lead region, the British Hollow Smelting Furnace had a 200-foot underground chimney. Owned by Thomas Hymer and Co., the blast furnace had one hearth with two fire pits in front, and handled ore from several area mines. You can still see its remains along the roadside.

Peering through the British Hollow smelting furnace

Directions:	Drive north from Potosi on State Hwy. 133 and turn right on Hippy Hollow Road; then, bear right at the intersection with British Hollow Road. The furnace is less than a mile from 133 on the left just past Church Road.
Contact:	See: www.grantcounty.org/tourism/historical-info-sites.

FOLKLORE VILLAGE
IOWA COUNTY

The past sometimes finds its way into our present lives in unexpected ways. Folklore Village brings to life the cultural heritages of many different ethnic groups, through festivals, folk dances, concerts, potlucks, and other events. Located on a former family farm, Folklore Village has grown to encompass an 1848 Norwegian immigrant home, one-room school, and 1882 church, in addition to Farwell Hall, a 5,500-square-foot facility offering two dance floors, kitchen, and classroom and exhibit spaces. Rustic bunkhouses provide overnight accommodations for weekend program participants. Yet unknown to many casual visitors, Folklore Village also has a connection to the lead mining era.

Beneath its Tall Grass Prairie Restoration Project (a partnership with the Wisconsin Department of Natural Resources, The Nature Conservancy, and the Prairie Enthusiasts) lies a network of old mining tunnels. The only tangible evidence can be found on the trail circling near the prairie's perimeter. Two wooden bridges span unseen openings into the old tunnels. As his Eagle Scout project, Michael Woolley constructed these bridges, along with four trail benches in 2005, with generous help from several local organizations and businesses.

Folklore Village bridge

"I chose to build this bridge because local organizations are always in need of someone willing to do volunteer work," Woolley said at an event celebrating the new bridge, as reported by *The Dodgeville Chronicle*. "This bridge is a structure that will be around for years to come and it will serve as a landmark of recognition for hard work and the dedication to the community that is provided by the Boy Scouts of America."

Directions:	Folklore Village is located at 3210 County Road BB, just off of U.S. Hwy. 18/151, between Ridgeway and Dodgeville, approximately forty miles west of Madison. Farwell Hall is on the west side of BB; watch for the sign. From the parking area, walk behind Farwell Hall past the playground and through the gate into the prairie. Turn right and follow the trail north. Keep following it when the trail turns left along the north property line to find the two bridges.
Seasons/ Hours:	Open year-round, dawn to dusk.
Length:	The longest bridge is about thirty feet long.
Contact:	Folklore Village, 3210 County Road BB, Dodgeville, WI 53533. Phone: 608/924-4000. Website: https://folklorevillage.org.

INTERSTATE STATE PARK
POLK COUNTY

The sadness sometimes sensed in Wisconsin's mining memories is perhaps most apparent along the Silverbrook Trail at Interstate State Park. Never a sure thing, the copper mining venture at the south end of the park led to several business failures.

Hezekiah Holbert and his wife, Fannie, came to the area from St. Paul, Minnesota, in the early 1890s. They built a magnificent summer house in 1895, with a massive stone fireplace and windows overlooking both the St. Croix River and the falls of Silver Brook. The mansion contained nineteen rooms and six bathrooms.

Over the years, Holbert drilled multiple shafts in search of elusive copper ore. But the rumored copper veins had never really existed. Instead, prospectors had only stumbled across occasional chunks carried to the area and deposited there by retreating glaciers.

Holbert's copper obsession "delayed the establishment of the Wisconsin Interstate Park," according to Rosemarie Vezina Braatz, whose historical essay appeared in the *Inter-County Leader* on August 19, 1998. When the state made plans to open the park in 1900, Holbert convinced Governor Robert LaFollette to order the

Mining pit, Interstate State Park

park commission to give him "a reasonable time to demonstrate his contention" that copper existed in the area.

Braatz further recorded this statement from a news item in the December 26, 1901 St. Croix Valley Standard: "on the Holbert place the diamond drill has brought up specimens that show forty or fifty dollars to the ton."

"Land abstracts show that the Holberts, in 1901, added six neighboring parcels of land to their original purchase," Braatz stated, "and in 1904, they deed[ed] their property to the Holbert Mining and Mercantile Company."

Yet four years later, apparently disillusioned, the Holberts sold the expanded Silverbrook property to the J.W. Coopers of the Griggs-Cooper Sanitary Foods Manufacturing Company of St. Paul. The Coopers held the property until 1919 when they sold it to Frank E. Ford, a St. Paul insurance and real estate dealer. Ford owned Silverbrook for another decade before selling to Robert Payne, affiliated with a Twin Cities brokerage firm. Payne held Silverbrook through the Great Depression, selling it to Frank Wukawitz and his wife, Agnes, in 1942.

After the decades of primarily personal use, Wukawitz converted the property for use as a ski resort, he clear-cut the timbered slope toward the river and developed three ski runs. But his venture would prove short-lived. The ski resort died with Wukawitz after its first season in the winter of 1955.

Next, Agnes signed a land contract with Annabell and James Rideaux of St. Paul in 1956. They converted Silverbrook into a country club for "colored people," one source told Braatz. The source also stated that Annabell "put so much money into restoring the house, and combined with other expenses and obligations, she just couldn't make it [and] Mrs. Wukawitz foreclosed."

Abandoned assayer's building, Interstate State Park

The lack of business success continued when a Los Angeles realtor, bought Silverbrook in 1962, only to sell it, finally, to the Wisconsin Department of Natural Resources in 1970. The state paid $90,000 to add the 197-acre property to Interstate Park.

Directions:	Located on State Hwy. 35 one half mile south of its intersection with U.S. Hwy. 8.
Seasons/ Hours:	Open year-round, from 6 a.m. to 11 p.m. Vehicle admission sticker required.
Length:	The Silverbrook Trail is about a mile and a quarter long, following part of the original road from St. Croix Falls to Osceola.
Precautions:	Stay on trails, some trails feature rough surfaces, steep drop-offs, and loose rocks.
Amenities:	Ice Age Interpretive Center with gift shop, restrooms, hiking, cross-country skiing, snowshoeing, camping, picnicking, fishing, hunting and trapping, swimming, boating, canoeing and kayaking, as well as rock climbing at your own risk. Rock climbing instructors should contact the park for a use permit; some areas are closed to climbing.
Contact:	Interstate State Park, 1275 State Hwy. 35, St. Croix Falls, WI 54024. Phone: 715/483-3747. Website: https://dnr.wi.gov/topic/parks/name/interstate.

Vacant and vandalized over many years, the Silverbrook mansion was deemed a hazard too costly to renovate and demolished in 1974. Still, mining ruins remain for hikers to find. Most impressive are the crumbling stone walls of the assay laboratory, a debris-filled shaft, and a nearby test pit. Remnants of the resort era remain too: Stone entrance pillars, an all-but-overgrown fountain, and cleared area around the former mansion are sad reminders of the resort and ski hill ventures.

Yet a hike to Silverbrook offers evidence of nature's redevelopment and the eighteen-foot Silverbrook Falls flows as reliably as ever. When you visit Interstate State Park, be sure not to miss the short Pothole Trail or others offering panoramic views of the bluff-walled St. Croix River. In addition, the Eagle Peak Trail, leading to the highest vantage point over the valley, passes a 1930's traprock quarry established by the Civilian Conservation Corps.

JACKSON COUNTY IRON MINE
JACKSON COUNTY

Two sites provide vistas of the former Jackson County Iron Mine, which operated by Inland Steel from 1969 to 1983. Bell Mound wayside, south of Black River Falls on I-94 westbound, features a trail to the top of the hill and overlook of the old mining

Bell Mound Scenic Overlook Trail

region. Wazee Lake Recreation Area, a Jackson County park, was established on the site of the former pit mine.

While the Bell Mound Scenic Overlook Trail is steep, it is, thankfully, paved, with a 550-foot boardwalk that makes the climb doable. At the top, the forest view makes the climb worthwhile, especially during fall colors, and benches provide a respite before standing up and loping downhill. During the summer, the wooded trail supplies welcome shade on hot days.

If you're in the mood to learn, signage near the base of the trail commemorates the area wildfires of April 27, 1997, and other historical markers honor veterans, law enforcement officers, and the passing of the passenger pigeon from the landscape.

Activity at the 1300-acre Wazee Lake Recreation Area centers around the 146-acre lake, formed when the iron mine closed, its pumps ceased, and the pit filled with water. With a depth of 355 feet, Wazee is the deepest inland lake in Wisconsin and attracts more than 1,000 scuba divers each year. Wazee (the name for "tall pine" comes from the Ho-Chunk language) offers divers the opportunity to gaze on underwater roads and other mine features, as well as platforms and fish cribs.

But you don't need to don scuba gear to learn about iron mining at Wazee. The magnitude of the lake gives some indication of the size of mining operations, and you can't miss the iron ore boulders featured throughout the park's landscape.

Former pit mine, now Wazee Lake

Mining began in this region in the 1850s but soon died. More than a century later, thanks to an increased demand for steel and newer technologies for extracting and using lower grade ore, the Jackson County Iron Mine opened and for a time prospered. Inland Steel shareholders approved a taconite facility at the site in 1967, which provided the only year-round source of ore by rail when Great Lakes shipping ports closed during the winter. The mine closed following a crash in U.S. steel markets.

Directions:	Wazee Lake Recreation Area is located at N6302 Brockway Rd, Black River Falls. From I-94, take Exit 116 to State Hwy. 54 toward Black River Falls. Turn right on West Bauer Road and then right again onto Brockway Road.
Seasons/ Hours:	Year-round, dawn to dusk. Attendants are on duty from Memorial Day through Labor Day. Vehicle admission fee. Additional fees for diving and camping.
Length:	The Bell Mound Scenic Overlook Trail measures perhaps one-third mile in length; the Wazee Lake Recreation Area trails total approximately nine miles.
Precautions:	Bell Mound Trail is steep. There are high bluffs and deep waters at Wazee Lake Recreation Area; several scuba diving fatal accidents have occurred here.
Amenities:	Hiking, biking, twelve rustic camping, picnicking, swimming beach, hunting, handicap accessible fishing pier, scuba diving, and non-motorized boating.
Contact:	Website: Jackson County Forestry and Parks Department, 307 Main St., Black River Falls, WI 54615. www.co.jackson.wi.us (search for "Wazee").

IRON COUNTY IRON MINING REMNANTS

Although you can no longer enter the old iron mines scattered throughout Iron County, you can still see vestiges of the industry that made Hurley and other northern Wisconsin towns booming and boisterous. You can reach several historic mine sites by driving along State Highway 77.

Beginning in Hurley, a stop at the Iron County Historical Society Museum, 303 Iron Street, provides an overview of the long history of mining in the area, up to the closing of the last mine in 1964. (Before you go, check out the museum's Facebook page.)

Also in Hurley, you can still walk along Silver Street, once home to various saloons and clubs of ill repute, where miners and lumberjacks spent much hard-earned money in their precious leisure time. Later during Prohibition, the Silver Street bars generally ignored the federal law, and gangsters like Al Capone visited the wild town. Tunnels beneath some establishments contained stills and served as escape routes when law enforcement officials staged raids.

For a different type of architecture, follow State Highway 77 west of Hurley and turn on Ringle Drive to see the art deco Cary Mine Building. From 1886 until it closed in 1964 the Penokee Iron Range mine produced high grade iron ore.

A short distance farther southwest on 77 brings you to Montreal, headquarters in the early 1900s of the Olgebay-Norton Mining Company, which owned the Montreal Mine. There are two sites worthy of note in Montreal. The first is the town itself, which features many white frame houses, curving streets, and careful landscaping. Montreal is a planned company town, built in 1921 to accommodate 700 miners and their families. The second site is a group of huge tailings piles, visible from Giles Falls Road and across the West Fork of the Montreal River from Giles Falls.

Continuing southwest, you soon come to Pence, where the Plummer Mine Headframe stands as the last remaining such structure in the state. Opened in 1904 and closed down in 1924, the shaft beneath the head-frame once extended almost half a mile beneath the surface. Cables running over the top of the headframe were attached to cars that carried miners into and out of the mine and also brought out the iron ore. The headframe anchors an interpretative park with exhibits and a Penokee Iron Range Historic Marker, part of the Iron County Heritage Area.

To the north, west of Hurley along U.S. Highway 2, a Wisconsin State Historic Marker commemorates the Gogebic Iron Range (an alternate Penokee name, especially in Michigan), which runs from Lake Namekagon, Wisconsin, to Lake Gogebic in Upper Michigan.

For a different kind of tour, check out Iron County's 300-plus-mile Pines and Mines mountain biking trail system. Cyclists can trace the rugged Penokee Range or visit historic mine sites. Website: https://www.travelwisconsin.com/mountain-biking/pines-mines-trail-13-204370.

MERRY CHRISTMAS MINE
IOWA COUNTY

Driving through southwestern Wisconsin's countryside, it's easy to think the land always looked as it does today: a patchwork of rolling hills, agricultural fields, and dark green woodlots, stitched together by silver streams. But the land hasn't always looked this way. The first Europeans found oak savannas—waving prairies interspersed with bur oak. "A world of grass and flowers stretched around me, rising and falling in gentle undulations," according to an early traveler quoted in the "Merry Christmas Mine Hill Visitor's Guide." In 1840, Eliza Steele described "whole acres of blossoms all bearing one hue, as purple, perhaps, or masses of yellow or rose; and then again a carpet of every color intermixed, or narrow bands, as if a rainbow had fallen on the verdant slopes."

Yet as early as the 1820s, miners began to alter this prairie paradise, ripping up the surface to search for lead, zinc, and copper, and stripping the hills of trees to burn in open smelters dug into the hillsides. As the miners searched deeper into the earth, shafts replaced surface diggings; and by the 1880s, windlasses, shaft houses, furnaces, piles of dirt, rock, and tailings littered the Southwest Wisconsin landscape.

While farms and cultivated fields have almost completely covered this early environmental devastation, tilling under the marks of one of the state's first mainstay

The mine hill is across the road from the main Pendarvis complex.

Above shaft number one on Merry Christmas Mine Hill

industries, scattered signs and scars till remain. The interpretative walking trails at the Merry Christmas Mine Hill point out some of these remnants of Wisconsin's rugged and rambunctious past. Managed by the Pendarvis State Historic Site of the Wisconsin Historical Society, the trails lead us into the Badger State's past—a past that's quite foreign to modern-day life in this unglaciated hill region. The hills themselves have changed since 1800—their surfaces marked by holes and unnatural piles, their insides tunneled and abandoned.

The trails meander through the restored prairie that now covers the former Merry Christmas Mine property, where displays of huge ore buckets, ore carts, machinery, ladders, and other equipment detail the history of mining in the area. There's information on badger holes and the stone remnants of a log furnace or open roasting hearth for processing the ore. More than 100 small, filled shafts and holes dot the hillside; and you can still see one intact shaft of the Merry Christmas Mine, a zinc mine begun by Isaac Suthers on December 25, 1905. The mine eventually comprised nine interconnected tunnels and operated for about ten years, reportedly closing after a fatal rock fall.

Accidents happened with some regularity on Merry Christmas Mine Hill, as they did at many other mines in the state. In 1907, an ore processing mill on this site was also destroyed, when dynamite, which was warming beneath a stove, exploded. The limestone Merry Christmas Mine building, however, still stands.

If you walk the trail from May through October, you may want to also take the Pendarvis tour of the restored Cornish homes, restaurant, and other buildings located across Shake Rag Street. (The name of this street dates to the era when wives would stand outside their homes and wave rags in the air to signal their menfolk to come home to dinner.) Dating from the 1830s, the distinctive limestone buildings preserve the history and culture of life in the lead boom. One early home, Polperro House, contains another type of underground attraction: a root cellar dug into the hillside.

From the distant top of the mine hill, the buildings appear like outcroppings on the steep hillside. In spring and summer gardens of hollyhocks, nasturtiums, poppies, violets, and other blooms surround the limestone buildings—bright decorations to light the way to a dim though not-so-distant past.

Directions:	Take U.S. 151 to Mineral Point. Near the north edge of town, turn on Shake Rag Street and watch for signs. The trails begin from the Pendarvis State Historic Site parking lot.
Seasons/ Hours:	While the trails are accessible year-round, Pendarvis State Historic Site is open from 9 a.m. to 5 p.m. daily from May 1 through October 31. There is a fee for tours of the miners' buildings, but no charge to visit the Pendarvis Museum Store on Spruce Street or to use the trails.
Length:	The half-mile Lead Trail passes seven marked stations and takes about thirty minutes. The Zinc Trail Loop also takes about thirty minutes, covering another half mile and featuring eight marked stations.
Precautions:	Despite the hillside location, the trails are not particularly steep and offer a fairly easy hike.
Amenities:	Picnicking, restrooms at Pendarvis, and many art galleries, antiques and gift shops in downtown Mineral Point.
Contact:	Pendarvis State Historic Site, 114 Shake Rag St., Mineral Point, WI 53565-0270. Phone: 608/987-2122. Website: https://pendarvis.wisconsinhistory.org/.

PERCIVAL MINE
DOUGLAS COUNTY

Hidden in the middle of Brule River State Forest, the ruins of Percival Mine give tangible evidence of a mine that employed eight to fifteen men in the 1870s. A copper vein was reportedly discovered in 1873, but after a year of exploration mining ceased. Still, we humans can be perseverant, and other mining attempts here occurred from 1899 through World War II.

The Historic Bayfield Road Trail leads hikers (and snowshoers in winter) past the mining site. The trail begins at the parking area on Clevedon Road and is partly a boardwalk. About a half mile from the trailhead, watch for a rocky hill on the left (north) with a fence on top. A short but very rugged, steep trail leads up to the board and wire fence, surrounding the water-filled mine shaft. Retracing your steps to the main trail, continue onward, descending to a wooden bridge that crosses an unnamed tributary of Percival Creek, which, in turn, runs into the Bois Brule. Not far after crossing this bridge, again watch on your left—this time for an old foundation, marking the likely former quarters of those 1870s miners.

Fence surrounding Percival Mine's water-filled shaft

From 1870 to 1885, the Historic Bayfield Road carried people, mail, and supplies between Superior and Bayfield before the railroad made travel so much easier. Today the Historic Bayfield Road Trail traverses a portion of the old road before heading through several drainages and mounting Sugar Camp Hill, where you may spot the Wisconsin Department of Natural Resources' Clevedon Fire Tower.

Directions:	To reach the Brule River State Forest headquarters, turn south on Ranger Road, just west of the town of Brule on U.S. 2. The parking area for the Historic Bayfield Road Trail is on the east side of Clevedon Road, which runs north from U.S. 2 west of the headquarters, at the western edge of the state forest.
Seasons/ Hours:	Open year-round, dawn to dusk.
Length:	Mine ruins are about a half mile along the trail from the parking area.
Precautions:	Trail features several steep, sometimes wet sections.
Amenities:	The Brule River State Forest contains forty-four miles of the Bois Brule River and offers trout fishing, river paddling, and hiking. It includes the Bois Brule Fish Hatchery and encompasses a sixteen-mile stretch of the North Country National Scenic Trail as well as eight miles of Lake Superior shoreline.
Contact:	Brule River State Forest, 6250 Ranger Rd., Brule, WI 54820. Phone: 715/372-5678. Website: https://dnr.wi.gov/topic/StateForests/bruleRiver.

RUSTIC ROAD 66
LAFAYETTE COUNTY

Amazingly a few vestiges of the lead mining era can still be seen in Southwest Wisconsin. For instance, Wisconsin Rustic Road 66 runs past piles of tailings and other remnants of the Kennedy Mine, which initially produced mostly lead, and then zinc as the mine deepened. Rustic Road 66 winds along short sections of Buncombe, Beebe, Ensch, and Kennedy roads, with the mine site on the west side of Kennedy. On the east side, the mine's disintegrating, brick electrical substation now has trees growing through it.

Mining at this site dates to the 1850s and by 1900 encompassed three separate mines, according to Loren Farrey in his book, A Tour Guide to the Mines of Lafayette County, Wisconsin (2001). The New Jersey Zinc Company purchased the mines and operated them under the Kennedy Mine name until 1919. Although an effort was made to reopen the mine during World War II, it failed as cave-ins occurred when water was once again pumped from the tunnels. The largest shaft measured 183 feet deep.

Former electrical substation for Kennedy Road mines

Every year spotting these mining remnants becomes more challenging, as nature reasserts itself, buildings collapse, and artifacts are buried beneath prairies, woodlands, and farm fields. Yet town names like Leadmine, New Diggings, and Mineral Point, along with street names like Roaster Road, will bear witness to the lead and zinc mining era long after most physical signs have disappeared.

One more town name deserves mention. If you drive west from Shullsburg on State Highway 11 and turn north on County I, you will soon reach Leadmine. In Leadmine, take Aetna Road for one mile east to reach the unincorporated town of Etna. Now primarily rolling countryside, a century and a half ago, the town boasted a gristmill, post office, store, and a hall with a seating capacity of 300, according to Farrey. The town served as a hub for workers at several nearby mines—including the Jug Handle Mine, Drybone Open Cut, and Empress Mine. The town name, Farrey reported, came "from its apparent resemblance to Sicily's Mount Etna volcano due the flames that shot high in the night sky from a lime kiln at the quarry."

Directions:	From State Hwy. 11 in Hazel Green, take County W east for roughly a mile and a half, and turn right (south) on Kennedy Road.
Length:	Kennedy Road runs about one and one third mile between County W and Buncombe Road.
Contact	http://wisconsindot.gov/Pages/travel/road/rustic-roads/rr66.aspx.

MICHIGAN'S UPPER PENINSULA COPPER AND IRON MINES

ompared to the family and small group operations of the early Southwest Wisconsin mines, the copper and iron mines of Michigan's Upper Peninsula seem gigantic in scope. Scores or hundreds of men working for the same mine at the same time could produce a small mountain of ore in the period that it took a handful of lead miners to fill a few ore buckets. While a single skilled miner could significantly contribute to a small mine's operation, the Upper Peninsula mines were more of a large group effort, demanding structures, engineering, labor relations, supervisors, and machine operators, among other specialists.

Yet, one of the Upper Michigan mines traces its roots to surface diggings that long predate Wisconsin's lead mining era. The Adventure Copper Mine owners have sought to connect mining's recent history with its prehistoric past, and this section begins with a description of the Adventure's history and two available tours. One of these wends around the outside of the mountain to view early digs, and the other goes through a tunnel in the middle of the mountain.

In contrast, the Delaware Copper Mine tour focuses exclusively on mining operations during the last half of the nineteenth century. During this period, the Delaware grew to encompass ten levels and reach a depth of 1,400 feet. Today, only the upper level is open to visitors; the remaining levels are below the water table. In fact, you can see the water in the second level, visible through a short, angled access tunnel leading down from the first level. You can also see huge rooms, or "stopes," carved out of the rock; early copper mining equipment; and the devastation caused by a fire at the base of one of the shafts. At its deepest point, the tour takes you 500 feet beneath the surface. Above ground, a short trail leads to ruined mine buildings, and a gift shop offers mining-related books, mineral samples, and plastic mining helmets for the kids.

Of the historic Upper Peninsula mines open to the public, only one is not a copper mine. The Iron Mountain Iron Mine, originally called the Vulcan Mine, opened in 1877 and shipped more than twenty-one million tons of ore before closing in 1945. The area open for tours is part of the oldest section of the mine, and you enter it via an open railcar pulled by a small electric locomotive. Highlights of a tour include an enormous stope, a pond filled with fish, and the site of a roof collapse.

The Quincy Mine is the largest of the accessible mines. In over 130 years of operation, it reached a depth of close to two miles (9,000 feet) and contained ninety-two levels. Only the uppermost levels are open for tours, which take you some 400 feet underground, including well beneath U.S. 41. When you "go to green" (return to the surface), you can tour exhibits and a gift shop located in several of the larger buildings comprising the mining complex. Possibly the most unforgettable feature of the Quincy tour is the trip to and from the mine opening, which you traverse in a glass-walled cog rail tramcar offering views of the Lake Superior shoreline.

MINNESOTA'S SOUDAN MINE

Wisconsin's other northern neighbor also offers an underground iron mine excursion, at Soudan Underground Mine State Park, about a two-hour drive north of Superior. You can enter a "cage" and journey more than 2,000 feet beneath the surface, and then ride a railcar for three quarters of a mile into the twenty-seventh level of the mine. Above ground, you can explore the dry house, drill shop, crusher house, and engine house.

The Soudan Mine began as a pit mine and shipped the first ore mined from Minnesota's Iron Range in 1884. When the company realized the ore body extended vertically into the earth rather than in a more horizontal layer, it switched to underground mining techniques. The mine operated until 1962, and a year later its owner, the U.S. Steel corporation, donated the Soudan to the state of Minnesota, which developed the site into a park.

Located on a ridge along the shore of Lake Vermilion, the park offers camping, fishing, hiking, and picnicking. To reach the park, drive north from Superior on U.S. 53 to Minnesota State Highway 169. Drive northeast to Soudan and watch for signs. To learn more, phone 218/753-2245 or visit www.dnr.state.mn.us/state_parks/lake_vermilion_soudan/tours.html.

ADVENTURE COPPER MINE
ONTONAGON COUNTY, MICHIGAN

Part archaeology, part geology, and part history, Adventure Copper Mine tours describe this land and its uses back several thousand years. In addition to documenting late-nineteenth-century copper mining here, two Adventure Mine tours provide a link to the distant mining past of early Native Americans and a glimpse of future development.

Adventure Mountain contains sites and pits where early Native Americans mined copper near the surface prior to 1200 B.C. More than two thousand years later, mid-nineteenth-century miners concentrated on some of these areas and also dug a number of exploratory shafts and tunnels. These explorations appeared to show that the copper in Adventure Mountain was located in scattered pockets, instead of veins that could be easily followed. As a result, the Adventure Mining Company developed a tribute system in 1855 to excavate the copper.

The company assigned interested miners to designated sites about the mountain and agreed to pay them $100 to $120 per ton of ore. More than fifty miners took up this challenge, producing more than 75,000 tons of ore the first year.

In 1863 the Adventure Mining Company was sold to the Adventure Copper Company, headed by Thomas F. Mason, president of the Quincy Mining Company, which created a mine that still bears its name. The new company located several copper veins after all and introduced more traditional mining methods—sinking additional shafts and digging many horizontal tunnels.

Today's Adventure tours take you into the mountain, to witness evidence of historical mining activity, which ended in 1920. The entire mine is unlit; visitors are issued hardhats with headlamps.

Four tours of different lengths showcase early mining activity. All explore stopes and other large open spaces where copper and silver were extracted. The most introductory tour, the Trammer's Tour, lasts from forty-five to sixty minutes. The Prospector's Tour lasts about an hour and twenty minutes; visitors hike past shafts to lower levels and see chunks of copper weighing hundreds of pounds left behind by the miners. There are no age restrictions for either of these tours.

A Miner's Tour adds a rappelling descent of eighty feet to a lower level of the mine, where visitors hike and crawl through the excavated tunnels. Near the end of this tour, visitors decide whether to cross a thirty-foot chasm via swing bridge or use a ten-foot slide to reach the exit. This tour lasts about three hours. Suggested minimum age is twelve.

Miner's Tour at Adventure Copper Mine (Photo: Adventure Mining Company)

The five- to six-hour Captain's Tour begins at 10 a.m. Eastern Time and includes a pasty lunch. Reservations are required; minimum age is thirteen. Participants each carry a ten-pound backpack and must be in good physical condition. This tour covers areas of the mine not seen on the Miner's Tour, where visitors see rails, carts, and other artifacts. As with the other tours, no mineral or artifact collecting is permitted.

Girl Scouts and Boy Scouts, college geology programs, and school classes can also make reservations for educational guided tours. In addition, six-hour drilling workshops provide a hands-on overview of mining, from hand drilling to the use of air compressors and pneumatic rock drills. Participants learn about the installation of rock bolts and other roof support technologies, as well as explosives theory and techniques.

The Adventure Mine attraction also offers approximately four miles of biking and hiking trails around the mine site, winding around old mine building foundations and historic pits. The route of the annual Miner's Revenge Bike Race (www.miners-revenge.com), held each July, incorporates 2000 feet of underground tunnels, from adit number one to adit number two. (An adit is a horizontal entrance to an underground passage, typically into the side of a mountain.) As the race website points out, the race takes riders three hundred feet beneath the surface, where "there's nobody to hear you scream."

John and Margaret Neph purchased the Adventure Mine property in 1972, opening it to the public a year later. The Neph's son, John, and his wife, Winnie offered tours until 2003. A year later, the Adventure Mining Company owned by Matthew and Victoria Portfleet purchased the mine and began offering tours in 2005.

Directions:	Take Michigan State Highway 38 for twelve miles east of Ontonagon; watch for signs to the mine.
Seasons/ Hours:	Open 9 a.m. to 6 p.m. Monday through Saturday; 11 a.m. to 6 p.m. on Sunday, from Memorial Day weekend to mid-October. (Closed on Wednesdays after Labor Day weekend.) Fee. Note: Ontonagon County observes Eastern Daylight Saving Time.
Length:	Tours range in length from less than an hour to six hours, covering up to several miles of passages.
Precautions:	Walking shoes (no clogs or sandals) and a light jacket are recommended. Temperature in the mine is forty-eight degrees year-round. The walking surface is uneven. On the longest tours you are up to forty minutes from the surface and assistance should a medical condition arise.
Amenities:	Camping, toilets, water, electricity, gift shop, hiking and biking trails.
Contact:	Adventure Copper Mine, 200 Adventure Rd., Greenland, MI 49929. Phone: 906/883-3371. Website: http://www.adventureminetours.com/.

DELAWARE COPPER MINE
KEWEENAW COUNTY, MICHIGAN

Horace Greeley, editor-owner of the *New York Tribune*, lived in Upper Michigan for a short time, where he served as president of the then-named North-West Mining Company. Writing to stockholders soon after the company's organization in 1847, he commented, "do not believe any profit ... can be made in mining copper." He complained that the costs of bringing the copper to the surface and processing it far exceeded earnings. Greeley was proved right. During its primary operating years of 1847-1887, the Delaware Copper Mine was reorganized, sold, or merged five times; in fact, financial problems were commonplace for many of the Upper Peninsula mines.

Today the 1400-foot-deep Delaware Copper Mine offers a singular opportunity for a less costly, self-guided tour of the historic mining passageways. Visitors begin by

Relic rails in Delaware Copper Mine (Photo courtesy of Delaware Copper Mine, Nick Adams Photography)

watching a short video of the mine before choosing their hardhat and walking behind the entrance building to enter an adit into the hillside.

Visitors climb down the stairs through the number one shaft, descending adjacent to the old skidway with tram rails still intact. The miners would load a skip, or tramcar, with ore and pull it to the surface along these rails.

Walking along the tunnel, or main drift, you pass several stopes, most larger than a house, from which the early miners excavated copper ore. Large timbers in the stopes appear to be ceiling supports but actually were installed to dampen the noise of the pounding and drilling. The stopes, hewn into hard conglomerate rock, do not require any support. To excavate the stopes, the miners set the ends of wooden beams into the walls and then laid planks across them to erect scaffolding, digging higher and higher into the ceiling.

Signs posted throughout the mine describe various mining operations and in the fall and spring you can sometimes spot hibernating bats. (Remember not to disturb them.) Also remember to bring a flashlight so that you can peer into several blocked-off tunnels.

Continuing along the drift, you see another short, diagonal tunnel leading to the level below. The miners dug these access tunnels as shortcuts, so they would not have to go all the way back to the shaft to ascend or descend to another level. Moving up or down the shaft during a shift when ore skips traveled there was also dangerous. You peer into the access tunnel and see a large, water-filled stope below. The Delaware's lower levels are all flooded. Scuba divers have explored many of the lower levels, and you can find several of their videos on YouTube.

After returning to the surface, visitors can stroll along a path on the other side of the gift shop to view the ruins of buildings once integral to the mining operations. The ruins of the 1870's hoist house and pump house are marked and identifiable. You can also see mining equipment and a collection of antique engines.

Directions:	Located twelve miles south of Copper Harbor on U.S. 41.
Seasons/ Hours:	Open 10 a.m. to 6 p.m. daily, mid-May through mid-October. Fee.
Length:	The quarter-mile tour lasts about forty-five minutes, depending on your interest level.
Precautions:	Temperature in the mine is forty-three degrees; a light jacket and walking shoes are recommended. The mine walkway is sometimes muddy. The ninety-one steps pose a problem for strollers.
Amenities:	Underground and aboveground picnic areas, gift shop, and walking trails; pet-friendly.
Contact:	Delaware Copper Mine Tours, HC1, Box 102, Mohawk, MI 49950. Phone in season: 906/289-4688. Website: http://www.delawarecopperminetours.com/.

MILLIE MINE BAT CAVE

A bat gate tops the shaft of the abandoned Millie Mine, protecting the bats and simultaneously allowing them access. Visit at dusk from April to May and September to October to view the bats. The site, a designated Michigan Wildlife Viewing Area, features a self-guided interpretative program.

The site is located in Iron Mountain on Park Avenue off of East A Street. Website: http://www.michigan.gov/dnr/0,4570,7-153-10370_12144-35558--,00.html, and Facebook: https://www.facebook.com/pages/Millie-Hill-Bat-Viewing-Area-/189268024536284.

IRON MOUNTAIN IRON MINE
DICKINSON COUNTY, MICHIGAN

Thanks to a colossal cutout image of "Big John"—a miner wearing boots that seemingly would hold Lake Wisconsin and hefting a pick the size of three trucks—you can't really miss Iron Mountain Iron Mine. Standing forty feet tall and weighing 2000 pounds, Big John holds sway over the parking lot, where loudspeakers blare Jimmy Dean's 1961 hit, Big Bad John, and the song Tennessee Ernie Ford made famous, Sixteen Tons.

Inside the mine building, long tables are laid with souvenir displays—rocks, minerals, fossils, mine helmets for the kids, books, candy, and crafts. At first glance, the exhibits resemble the 4-H building during a Wisconsin county fair. In addition, two display cases feature such mining artifacts as the Penn Iron Mining Company's payroll ledger from 1891.

Originally called the Vulcan Mine, the Iron Mountain Iron Mine began operations in 1877 and shipped more than twenty-one million tons of ore before closing in 1945. Open for tours since 1958, the accessible passages are part of the oldest section of the mine.

You join other tour participants in an area beyond the display tables to don a hardhat and yellow rain jacket. You select a hat, adjusting it to more or less fit your head, and then slip on one of the flashy jackets.

The tour begins with an examination of an array of mining equipment and machinery. For example, there is a compressed-air engine with a bucket in front designed to scoop the ore, lift it over the engine and operator, and then drop it into a car behind the engine.

From here, everyone proceeds to a narrow-gauge track. You board one of several small, open passenger cars, where you sit facing sideways along one bench that runs the length of the car. An electric locomotive pulls your train into a tunnel opening into the side of a hill. The tunnel, timbered with tamarack, was built in 1870 and shut down in 1888.

The train moves forward slowly, stopping periodically so the tour guide can point out different mineral formations and signs of early mining. Compared to the lead mines of Southwest Wisconsin, this mine tunnel is higher, wider, and far deeper. At the deepest point of the tour, it is more than 400 feet below the surface.

A quarter of a mile into the tunnel, everyone disembarks to further explore on foot in the semi-gloom. Gravel and mud alternately crunch and squish beneath your feet. The tunnel is approximately seven feet in height.

The tunnel eventually leads to two stopes. Little Stope was closed in 1889 and rediscovered in 1956. Big Stope is aptly named: The vast room stretches 630 feet in length, with a width of 300 feet and a height of 180 feet. In the far distance, a duplicate cutout of Big John appears miniscule in the sweep of the stope.

In the late 1880s, the early miners worked in the dimness of candlelight. For a few moments, your guide turns off the electric lights, and you can't imagine anything blacker. Early miners sometimes measured the passing of time by the number of candles they burned: since one candle burned about an hour, an eight-candle shift was an eight-hour day.

Dr. Nelson P. Hulst directed the first substantial prospecting by the Milwaukee Iron Company and in 1872 discovered the East Vulcan Mine (Iron Mountain Iron Mine), which began producing in 1877. During the prospecting era, the company hauled ore to Menominee by wagon and-then shipped it out on the Great Lakes. "After 1877, ore was shipped to Escanaba on the 'new' Chicago and NorthWestern Railway," according to the attraction's website. At its peak production, the mine employed 1,500 men.

The final underground tour stop is in a huge cavern created when the roof of the mine collapsed. The size of the boulders and the enormity of the black space suggest a power that can move mountains in an instant. It's definitely time to head back to daylight. You turn and retrace your steps to the waiting train.

Once more on the surface, you blink in even the light on an overcast day and head indoors to doff your helmet and jacket and peruse the souvenir tables one last time. Nestled in a planter or turned into a bookend, a chunk of dusty red iron ore will serve as a gritty reminder of your iron mine expedition.

Directions:	Drive nine miles east of Iron Mountain, Michigan, on U.S. 2.
Seasons/ Hours:	Open daily, 9 a.m. to 5 p.m. Central Standard Time, from Memorial Day weekend through October 15. Fee.
Length:	You explore about a half mile of tunnels by electric train and on foot. The tour lasts approximately one hour.
Precautions:	Wear walking shoes, since the walkways can be muddy and slick underfoot. Although you will be supplied with a rain jacket, you may want to wear a sweater underneath; the temperature in the mine is forty-three degrees year-round.
Amenities:	A drinking fountain at the building entrance offers cold water piped from within the mine; restrooms, gift shop advertising the largest rock in Upper Michigan and free coffee and cookies.
Contact:	Iron Mountain Iron Mine, P.O. Box 216, Iron Mountain, MI 49801. Phone in season: 906/563-8077. Website: http://ironmountainironmine.wixsite.com/ ironmine.

OLD VICTORIA MINERS VILLAGE
ONTONAGON COUNTY, MICHIGAN

Ancestors of Native Americans once dug surface copper mines west of present-day Rockland, Michigan, one of the first areas prospected by Europeans. The area's fame grew as the location of the 3,708-pound Ontonagon Boulder, discovered in the west branch of the Ontonagon River. A glacier likely carried the immense copper boulder to the site about twenty miles upriver from Lake Superior. Today the Ontonagon Boulder is held by the Smithsonian Museum of Natural History.

Originally begun as the Cushin Mine, the Victoria Mine operated here from 1849 to 1921, finally shutting down when the price of copper fell after World War I. By then, the company town near the mine had grown to number eighty houses, along with a school and general store. Initially called Finn Town, Victoria also welcomed miners from such places as Austria, Canada, Cornwall, Croatia, Italy, and Sweden. When the mine closed, the miners and their families moved away, the buildings falling into disrepair.

Half a century later, the Society for Restoration of Old Victoria began restoring a few buildings and opened the site for public tours in 1976. Today visitors can tour four restored and furnished 1899 buildings, including two boarding houses and one single-family cabin. Visitors can also walk about the former mine site and find several cabin foundations, the remains of the hoist house, and other ruins in the woods. The Society hosts a craft fair in August and other public events.

Directions:	Old Victoria Miners Village is located at 25401 Victoria Dam Rd, Rockland, MI 49960. Take U.S. 45 to Rockland and turn west on Elm Street, which becomes Victoria Dam Road outside of town. The village is about four miles from Rockland.
Seasons/ Hours:	Memorial Day weekend through mid-October, from 11 a.m. to 5 p.m. daily. Suggested donation: $2.00.
Contact:	Phone: 906/886-2617. Website: https://www.facebook.com/oldvictoria.

QUINCY MINE
HOUGHTON COUNTY, MICHIGAN

Approaching the Quincy Mine, a National Historic Landmark, the first thing you notice is the shaft house, unprepossessing and resembling most others you've seen abandoned on Upper Michigan hillsides. Yet this shaft house serves as the entrance to a mammoth mining and museum complex, including a hoist tower, museum building, and gift shop. You also can see the foundations of a blacksmith shop, boiler house, stamp mill (where the ore was broken up), railroad turntable, and engine house.

Organized in 1846 and operated until 1980, the Quincy Mine provides an excellent history of more than 130 years of copper mining on the Keweenaw Peninsula. By the time it closed, the mine had reached a depth of about 9000 feet (one and three quarter miles) and contained ninety-two levels. Each drift—or horizontal tunnel—was about six feet high and four feet wide.

Only the uppermost levels are accessible, and tours take visitors some 400 feet underground. Descending much farther would be difficult, since the mine is filled with water below the seventh level. When in operation, pumps worked continuously to empty the lower levels.

The temperature in the upper levels is quite cool; however, miners working deep in the mine noted that the temperature climbed as they headed downward, until it was ninety degrees at the lowest level. The dangers of mining seem especially evident in this large mine; and, indeed, 253 miners died at Quincy during its operation, due to cave-ins, falls, fires, explosions, and other accidents.

Not that mining has ever been viewed as a glamorous job. Many copper miners developed bad hearing, poor eyesight, and worse conditions from working deep beneath the surface. For many years, the Quincy miners worked a twelve-hour shift, while actually being paid for only ten hours. The trip down into the mine took one hour, and the trip back out—sometimes called "going to green"—took another hour. The miners were not paid for this "commuting" time.

Today, visitors commute to the mine in style, riding down the Quincy hill aboard a cog rail tram, with large windows providing spectacular views of the peninsula. From this sky train, you can see the Huron Mountains, the city of Houghton, and the lift bridge that spans the Portage Canal, separating Houghton from Hancock, Michigan.

At the bottom of the hill, you disembark the tram to board a wagon pulled by a small tractor. Your wagon then enters the Quincy via an expanded adit, originally built in 1892 to drain water out of the mine. Almost immediately, you notice the tempera-ture drop and are thankful for the wool-lined coat you were issued earlier, along with the required hardhat. Today a five-mile-per-hour breeze moves through the adit, creating a small chill factor. When the mine was in operation, there was a continuous twenty-five-mile-per-hour wind blowing through all the tunnels from multiple shafts. Only two grated shafts are currently open for ventilation.

The tractor and wagon move easily along the adit, which has been expanded to fifteen feet high and fifteen feet wide by Michigan Technological University students. Michigan Tech still uses the mine; and you pass an underground classroom carved out of one side of the tunnel.

You ride underneath U.S. 41, then disembark from the wagon and walk to Shaft Number Five. Your guide shows various mining tools and explains how some of them work. He turns on a power drill for a few seconds, and the children in your group hold their ears as the sound reverberates through the tunnel.

Watching your step on the mud and gravel floor, you move farther into the tunnels. Along the way, you note more equipment and signs of miners long passed from the scene.

Examining some drill patterns on the walls, you learn that miners often drill holes in a four-square pattern, with more holes placed near the center of the pattern. The miners would explode the center holes first, then the second ring, with the outer ring exploding last. The resulting implosion meant that rock broken from the later blasts would fall into the center hole instead of scattering up and down the tunnel.

A few visitors have begun to shiver, and it's time to retrace your steps back to the wagon for the return journey under the highway and back to the tram waiting at the base of the hill. The ride up the hill is just as breathtaking as it was on the way down and helps acclimate you to life topside.

Following the mine tour, you explore the museum in the 1892 hoist house, containing drills, blacksmith tools, a 300-pound piece of sheet copper, and a model of the mining operations, among other displays. By far the most impressive exhibit is the largest steam-powered hoist engine ever built. Filling a several-story room, the Nordberg steam hoist weighs 1.65 million pounds and has a drum measuring thirty feet in diameter. Twenty tons of steel cable were once wrapped around that drum.

The cables exited the hoist house through an opening in the wall near the top of the building and then moved over a series of high A-frames outside until reaching the shaft house. The miners always located the shaft house at some distance from the hoist house, because when the hoist engine ran, its vibrations would have caused rocks to fall in the shaft, had it been sited directly above. Over the years it operated, the Quincy Mine had eight to ten shaft house/hoist house combinations.

Adjacent to the parking area, the renovated shaft house contains a small eating area on the ground floor. Here you can watch a video depicting Upper Michigan copper mining and featuring many historical photos.

The Quincy Mine is owned and operated by the Quincy Mine Hoist Association, a 501©(3) nonprofit organization, supported by volunteers and several private and public organizations. It's operated in cooperation with the Keweenaw National Historical Park.

Directions:	Take U.S. 41 north through Hancock, Michigan.
Seasons/ Hours:	Open May to mid-June, Friday through Sunday, 9:30 a.m. to 5 p.m.; open daily mid -June through mid-October, 9:30 a.m. to 5 p.m.; limited hours in off-season. Fee.
Length:	The full tour takes visitors more than a half mile into the mine on the seventh level and can take up to two hours.
Precautions:	Temperature in the mine is forty-three degrees. Wear walking shoes, as walkways in the mine can be muddy.
Amenities:	Restrooms, gift shop in the restored 1894 supply house; varied opportunities for dining and sightseeing in Hancock and Houghton.
Contact:	Quincy Mine Hoist Association, 49750 US Highway 41, Hancock, MI 49930. Phone: 906/482-3101. Website: http://www.quincymine.com/.

SECTION THREE

TUNNELS AND OTHER
MANMADE UNDERGROUND SPACES

WISCONSIN'S RESTORED RAILROAD DEPOTS

Railroading has long captured the imagination of Wisconsin travelers and preservationists, and the state boasts a large number of restored depots. Many now house railroading and local history museums. For instance, the Railroad Memories Museum has found a home in the former Chicago & Northwestern depot in Spooner, featuring eight rooms of railroad equipment, books, and track inspection vehicles. You also can view railroading videos and two model train displays. The Gresham Depot Museum in Gresham displays such memorabilia as railroad lanterns and telegrapher's equipment and the Gordon-Wascott Historical Museum and Depot in Gordon includes the town's Soo Line depot, built in 1912.

Several depots have been converted to other public uses. The Mazomanie Free Library moved to that town's restored depot in 1992. The wood frame building dates to the mid-nineteenth century and may be one of the oldest wooden depots in the state. Also in Dane County, the Waunakee Chamber of Commerce occupies the restored depot originally constructed in 1903. And the Wisconsin Department of Natural Resources restored the Kendall Depot to serve as headquarters for the Elroy-Sparta Trail. Many of the restored depots are not in full-time use but are open to the public primarily on weekends or during special events.

Tunnels—manmade underground passages through soil or rock—have been around almost as long as humankind. Early cave dwellers likely added to their homes or dug connecting tunnels between nearby caves; and there is evidence of tunnels in Babylonia, Thebes, Egypt, and the Roman Empire. People in ancient times constructed tunnels for the same kinds of purposes for which we use them today: transportation, storage, mining, and water and sewer mains.

Since exploring a utilities tunnel is usually neither accessible nor desirable, this section focuses on other historic tunnel uses. Also excluded are certain modern highway conveniences, such as automobile underpasses and pedestrian tunnels connecting modern buildings. The following entries also showcase tunnels that are accessible to most people and have an interesting history or story to tell.

RAILROAD TUNNELS

The Milwaukee Road constructed possibly the first tunnel in Wisconsin—and the first of several near Tunnel City in Monroe County—in 1861. The railroad used this tunnel until 1874, replacing it two years later with another that's still in use today. All told, regional railroads like Milwaukee Road, Chicago & Northwestern, and Illinois Central built close to a dozen tunnels in Wisconsin from about 1879 to 1920. Smaller, local lines also sometimes constructed tunnels. Though less well documented, these tunnels sometimes can be spotted in hilly terrain, and old-timers will occasionally tell you about Buncombe or another long-abandoned example.

Railroad companies generally built tunnels—and trestles, for that matter—to even out a steep grade, not as a shortcut through a steep hill. The low grades of the rail corridors have continued to prove useful, as some have been converted to multi-use recreational trails. Even children can easily bike along these trails; and the lack of vehicular traffic makes them all the more attractive for family bicycle outings.

WISCONSIN UNDERGROUND

ELROY-SPARTA STATE TRAIL
JUNEAU AND MONROE COUNTIES

The three tunnels on the Elroy-Sparta State Trail played an important role in the state's early economic development. All were completed in the 1870s, just a few years after the golden spike connected the two sections of the nation's first transcontinental railroad in Promontory, Utah, in 1869. Crews sometimes worked around the clock tio construct the tunnels, using only hand tools, horses, and oxen.

The tunnels were used until the Chicago & Northwestern Railroad (C&NW) abandoned the line in 1964. During the 1920s, the railroad was utilizing at least seven tunnels in the state, but that number began to decline by the 1930s. The C&NW finally merged with the Union Pacific Railroad in 1995.

Several of Wisconsin's old railroad tunnels have collapsed; others have been daylighted, or opened up. But hikers and bikers can still experience traversing four of the old C&NW tunnels: the three on this trail as well as one on the Omaha County Trail. The three stone and brick tunnels are interspersed along this trail near Kendall, Wilton, and Norwalk and are accessible from several points along the thirty-two-mile path. The longest is the one at Norwalk, which runs almost three quarters of a mile; sometimes you cannot see the end of the tunnel before you.

Walking through them is a great way to cool down on a hot summer day and connect with both the workers who dug their way into these hills less than a decade after the Civil War and the generations of railroaders who used them for almost a century afterward. As you enter the dark passages, you will notice the giant wooden doors once used to shutter the tunnels in winter, preventing ice from building up inside.

Tunnels aside, the rest of the Elroy-Sparta State Trail is a delight for all ages. Biking its length, you encounter more than thirty trestles and views featuring lush fields, rocky bluffs, and wooded slopes; yet the three percent maximum grade is easy for bikers of all ages. The first rails-to-trails conversion in the United States, the Elroy-Sparta Trail project was established in 1965 and opened to bikers in 1967. To learn more about the history of the trail, its tunnels, and railroading in Wisconsin, visit the museum at trail headquarters in Kendall.

A number of area retailers sell permits, and several bike shops offer rentals and shuttle services along the trail. To learn more about area attractions, visit the website of the Friends of the Elroy-Sparta State Trail: http://elroyspartatrail.com/.

134

Tunnel Number Three on the Elroy-Sparta State Trail (Photo: Sparta Chamber of Commerce)

Directions:	The trail generally runs near State Highway 71 for most of its distance and can be entered from State Highway 71 at several locations—a half mile northeast of Elroy, at the trail headquarters in the old Kendall Depot, at Wilton, at Norwalk, or southeast of Sparta near the intersection of State Highways 16 and 71.
Seasons/ Hours:	Visitors can hike, bike, or in winter snowmobile on the trail. Passes are not necessary to hike or snowmobile on the trail but are required for all bikers age sixteen and over.
Length:	Tunnels near Kendall and Wilton are a quarter mile long; tunnel near Norwalk is the longest in the state—almost three quarters of a mile.
Precautions:	If you bike the trail, be prepared to walk your bicycle through the tunnels, which have an average temperature of abut fifty degrees. A flashlight or bike headlamp will come in handy.
Amenities:	Summit Rest Area, near Tunnel Three, northwest of Norwalk, offers picnic tables, toilets, and a soda machine. The Wisconsin Department of Natural Resources operates backpack campgrounds near both ends of the trail. The towns along the way (Elroy, Kendall, Wilton, Norwalk, and Sparta) offer a variety of food, camping, lodging, and other facilities for bikers and hikers. The Wilton Lions Club even offers a pancake breakfast, 7 a.m. to 10:30 a.m. Sunday mornings at the village park from Memorial Day through Labor Day. Tunnel Trail Campground (http://www.tunneltrail.com) near Wilton offers trail access, bike rentals, and camping.
Contact:	Elroy-Sparta State Trail Headquarters, P.O. Box 297, Kendall, WI 54638. Phone: 608/463-7109. Website: http://dnr.wi.gov/topic/parks/name/elroysparta/.

OMAHA COUNTY TRAIL
JUNEAU COUNTY

Carved through a steep hillside, the tunnel on the Omaha County Trail is one the former Omaha line of the Chicago & Northwestern Railroad running thirteen miles between Camp Douglas and Elroy. Contrary to some published maps, the tunnel is located close to four miles south of Hustler at County Highway S. In fact, the highway runs over the top of the tunnel at a right angle to the trail—making it a bridge over the trail as well as a tunnel through the hill. Built in 1876, the tunnel likely predates the county highway construction by a number of years.

The Omaha County Trail opened in 1992 and is accessible year-round. It stretches through woods, farmlands, and bluff country.

You may want to plan your visit to this trail to coincide with one of annual celebrations along its path. The Elroy Fair takes place in June, and Hustler hosts the three-day Hustlerfest each August. Camp Douglas supports its neighboring state military installations (Camp Williams and Volk Field) by celebrating Armed Forces Day each year the weekend prior to Memorial Day weekend.

Trail passes are available from several businesses in these three towns: Elroy Trail Commons and Hansen's IGA also in Elroy, the Hustle Inn and Hustle Stop in Hustler, and the Camp Douglas Travel Mart.

Directions:	The trail runs from Camp Douglas through Hustler to Elroy, where it connects with the Elroy-Sparta and The 400 state trails. You also can reach the tunnel by biking or hiking three and three-fourths miles south from Hustler.
Seasons/ Hours:	Open year-round; however, ice accumulates in the tunnel during the winter months. Pass required for bicyclists over age sixteen.
Length:	The tunnel runs 875 feet through a hill. The trail is thirteen miles long.
Precautions:	Bring a flashlight.
Amenities:	This trail is paved. There is a rest area with picnic tables, water, and toilets on the trail just north of the tunnel. The trail towns of Camp Douglas, Hustler, and Elroy offer parks and restaurants.
Contact:	Juneau County Land, Forestry and Parks Department, 650 Prairie St., Mauston, WI 53948. Phone: 608/847-9389. Website: http://www.co.juneau.wi.gov/trails.html.

STEWART TUNNEL
GREEN COUNTY

Variously known as Exeter Tunnel and Belleville Tunnel, Stewart Tunnel is located south of Belleville, east of New Glarus, and north of Monticello, on the Badger State Trail. The trail follows the former Illinois Central Railroad line and runs from Madison south to the Wisconsin-Illinois border, where it connects to the Jane Addams Trail ending in Freeport, Illinois.

Construction on the line began in 1886; construction on the tunnel began in December that year from both the north and south ends. The tunnel is named for the project's contractor, James Stewart of Pennsylvania, who was thrown from a buggy and killed when he was following the proposed route of the new line.

The contractors and engineers built a headquarters, which served as an office and sleeping quarters, on the summit of the hill. The workers could rent shanty-type lodging nearby for $3.50 per week. They at first earned $1.25 per day; after a strike, wages rose to $1.75 per day. Using hand drills, the workers made holes in the limestone for explosives; they removed the rock with a hoisting apparatus and a steam shovel at each end. Steam-powered, and later compressed-air drills, were also used. The two groups of workers completed the tunnel in December 1887, meeting perfectly in the middle.

Illinois Central, owner of the line, merged with the Gulf Mobile & Ohio to form Illinois Central Gulf in 1972. Six years later the South Central Wisconsin Rail Transit Commission was created when Dane and Green counties contracted to continue rail service between Madison and Freeport. Illinois Central Gulf Railroad sold the line in 1980, and a short line railroad, the Wisconsin and Calumet, operated it beginning in February 1981. For a variety of reasons, however, needed work on the line was not completed, and most of the line was embargoed in December 1993.

Four years later, the Department of Natural Resources began to consider converting the corridor to a recreational trail under the federal Rails to Trail Act and in 2006 a master plan was approved. The Badger State Trail opened in 2010. During the late 1990s Stewart Tunnel had been accessible only via speeder cars during Green County's annual Depot Days, and after 1999 was closed during trail planning and development.

The most interesting feature of the tunnel is that it is curved. Entering it, you cannot see daylight from the opening at the opposite end, although you can sometimes see a slight glow ahead. Stewart Tunnel is 1,200 feet long.

Directions:	From Monticello, take County Highway C northwest to County Highway CC, driving north to Tunnel Road. Turn left on Tunnel Road and drive one block. The tunnel is approximately one eighth mile to the south.
Seasons/ Hours:	Open year-round. Pass not required for hikers and joggers. Pass required for other activities by individuals age sixteen and older.
Length:	The tunnel is about 1,200 feet long.
Precautions:	A six-mile section of the Badger State Trail between Madison and Purcell Road is surfaced with asphalt and is suitable for in-line skating. Snowmobiling and some winter ATV use is permitted; see website for restrictions.
Amenities:	Belleville's Library Park is next to the trail and offers parking, picnic tables, and a water fountain. Monticello, Belleville, and New Glarus offer a variety of shops and restaurants, including those celebrating New Glarus's Swiss heritage.
Contact	Badger State Trail, W5508 CTH NN, New Glarus WI 53574. Phone: 608/527-2335. Website: http://dnr.wi.gov/topic/parks/name/badger/.

UNDERGROUND SPACES: PEOPLE AND PRODUCTS

Wisconsin has oodles of manmade tunnels. Yet a large number are privately held and as inaccessible as the majority of the state's caves and mines. Some—for example, those connecting buildings on college or business campuses—are not particularly captivating. Others—like the utilities tunnels running beneath many cities—are not particularly inviting, although "urban caving" has its fans. (Look elsewhere for information on the tunnel between Milwaukee's Sacred Heart Center and the St. Joseph Center or for a map of the University of Wisconsin-Madison utilities tunnels.)

So what makes a tunnel intriguing? A longer tunnel is not necessarily more interesting than a short one, as some of the examples here demonstrate. But what really sets one tunnel apart from another is often its appearance or purpose. The tunnels described met different needs. Some served—and still serve—as storage facilities. Others offered an escape route in time of attack or pursuit. And still others provided a somewhat uncertain use related to a particular individual or company's needs.

All of the tunnels covered here are relatively short; most are less than fifty feet in length. And all offer in some measure a passageway to our past, a way to explore our own Wisconsin roots and shared heritage. Delving into their mysteries can result in surer relationships with our forebears, our grandparents, our parents, and ourselves. Exploring them either on our own or with a child in tow can be fun to boot.

HOUSE CAVE

One Wisconsin caver discovered House Cave partway up a sandstone bluff along a state highway. The original opening had been expanded into two rooms and was now U-shaped, with two entrances appearing above the highway. There were still a few small pieces of furniture in the "house," apparently abandoned some time ago. Although this home provided shelter, it offered little in the way of modern conveniences.

From time to time, stories circulate about people having lived in Wisconsin caves. According to one report, Chinaman's Bluff, in the vicinity of Target Bluff near Camp Douglas, was so named because a Chinaman lived in a cave in the bluff for a time.

Other stories tell of people who have burrowed into a hillside in a remote spot, to camp for a season or two beneath the earth and save on rent money. Maybe the individual is a hermit or simply a student too poor to pay for a University of Wisconsin residence hall room. But, so far, no Wisconsin story compares to that of Thomas Johnson, who was evicted in 1999 from his home of ten years: a bunker on Nantucket Island off the coast of Massachusetts. His abode contained Belgian stone floors, cedar paneling, a queen-size bed, and skylights. Johnson bragged about his cliff dwelling in the Catskills and a bunker near a waterfall in Pennsylvania.

These stories surprise most Americans. Yet, people in many countries still live in excavated homes or caves. A number of families in Tunisia live in excavated, communal underground dwellings that feature smaller rooms off of a central courtyard. In China, millions of people reside in caves in the Yellow River Valley. Maybe House Cave isn't such a bad idea, after all.

BLACK POINT ESTATE ROOT CELLAR
WALWORTH COUNTY

If there's a top ten contest for Wisconsin root cellars, Black Point Estate's entry would likely head the list. Built in 1888 to preserve foods for the Conrad Seip family at their Lake Geneva mansion, the root cellar measures thirty-three feet long by eleven feet wide and nine feet high. Three-tiered metal racks line the two side walls resembling bunk beds for produce. Two circular air vents can be opened to allow the cool temperatures of fall nights to descend into the cellar. Seven cement steps lead down into the cellar, which was protected by three separate doors.

Once the summer home of Chicago brewery owner Seip and his descendants, Black Point Estate and Gardens is now a Wisconsin Historic Site, open to visitors from spring through fall. The thirteen-bedroom Queen Anne mansion and its large gardens rest on twenty-eight wooded acres atop the bluff overlooking the lake. Visitors arrive via a Geneva Lake Guide boat tour (http://www.genevalakeguide.com/) and a 120-stair climb up to the estate. The remarkable root cellar is one stop on the Black Point Nooks and Crannies tour, which offers a behind-the-scenes look into the mansion lifestyle. These in-depth tours extend to the basement and third floor of the mansion and take place every Friday from June through August. They describe the production of electricity for the mansion and other technologies that made life there comfortable.

Long hidden on the mansion grounds, the cellar was rediscovered beneath the leaves by Jim Beloian, local historian, tour boat captain, and Black Point Estate guide. Beloian has conducted hundreds of tours of Black Point Estate, as well as other boat and shoreline walking tours.

Black Point Estate root cellar is thirty-three feet long

Directions:	The Nooks and Crannies tour begins at the Riviera Docks at 812 Wrigley Drive in downtown Lake Geneva.
Seasons/ Hours:	June through August, Fridays, 10:30 a.m. to 2 p.m. Fee.
Precautions:	While the mansion's first floor is wheelchair accessible, Nooks and Crannies tours involve many stairs—call for additional accessibility information. Only the Nooks and Crannies tour provides a look at the root cellar.
Amenities:	Other boat and shoreline walking tours are available and the city of Lake Geneva offers a variety of dining and shopping opportunities. Nearby attractions include Big Foot Beach State Park and Yerkes Observatory.
Contact	Phone: 262-248-1888. Websites: https://blackpointestate.wisconsinhistory.org and https://www.wisconsinhistory.org/calendar/event/5863/black-point-nooks-and-crannies.

CEDAR CREEK WINERY
OZAUKEE COUNTY

The stone and tamarack building now home to Cedar Creek Winery began as a woolen mill in 1864. The fifty horsepower generated by the creek ran more than twenty looms and knitting machines, which worked to fill the demand for wool products during the Civil War. A generation later the mill had the first electricity in Cedarburg, when the owners installed a water-powered generator to provide electricity to the mill and their own nearby homes.

Following the rise in popularity of synthetic fabrics, the woolen mill closed in 1969. Threatened by the wrecking ball by 1971, the mill was saved when Jim and Sandra Paper stepped in, renovating it and several nearby buildings to house the Newberry and later the Stone Mill Winery along with a group of owner-operated restaurants, shops, and studios.

The Wollersheim family, owner of Wollersheim Winery in Prairie du Sac, purchased the business in 1990, renaming it Cedar Creek Winery. Touring it today, you can see the quarried limestone, the huge tamarack timbers harvested from area bogs, and the cellars where quality wines now age slowly in oak barrels.

You also can see the entrance to a tunnel that once ran under the street. Sealed off in the late 1990s by Cedarburg's utility department, the tunnel's exact purpose is unknown, though it definitely dates from the years when the building was in use as a woolen mill.

When you have completed your winery tour, including samples of wine and wine products, you may want to allot some time to tour the other shops and galleries in the Cedar Creek Settlement. Although there are no other tunnels to investigate, you can continue to explore Wisconsin's past in antiques shops or examine the mysteries of modern artists' creativity in several galleries. Beyond the settlement, Cedarburg contains many other buildings constructed from limestone quarried nearby and features a covered bridge dating to 1876.

Directions:	Located at the intersection of Washington Avenue and Bridge Road. From the south, take I-43 to exit 89. Follow County Highway C to State Highway 57 (Washington Avenue) into Cedarburg and continue straight on Washington Avenue when State Highway 57 veers off to the right. Continue to Bridge Road. From the north, follow State Highway 57 into town, turn right on Bridge Road, and continue to Washington Avenue and the winery.
Seasons/ Hours:	Open year-round, from 10 a.m. to 5 p.m., Sunday through Thursday, and 10 a.m. to 6 p.m., Saturdays and Sundays. Fee.
Length:	The tour lasts forty-five minutes to an hour.
Amenities:	Cedar Creek Winery is located in Cedar Creek Settlement, which also house several restaurants, antiques stores, and arts and crafts galleries.
Contact:	Cedar Creek Winery, N70 W6340 Bridge Rd., Cedarburg, WI 53012. Phone: 800/827-8020 or 262/377-8020. Website: http://cedarcreekwinery.com.

CRAWFORD COUNTY HISTORIC JAIL
CRAWFORD COUNTY

Time has done nothing to make the 1867 Crawford County Jail appear more inviting. Though never designed to accommodate prisoners for more than a short period, its seven-by-five-foot cells with double metal bunks seem wretched by today's standards. Two of the cells, designed for solitary confinement, were equipped with leg irons and arm chains and had no outside light. Two smaller cells lacked bunks and were apparently used for temporary confinement. One can only wonder about the conditions of the previous 1843 Wisconsin Territorial Prison, which the 1867 dungeon replaced. Though lighting has been installed and cement now covers the old pebble floors, these improvements cannot mask the misery of this jail.

Directions:	Prairie du Chien is on the Mississippi River at the intersections of U.S. 18 and State Highways 27 and 35. In downtown Prairie du Chien, from East Wisconsin St./State Hwy. 60/27, turn right onto South Beaumont Road.
Seasons/ Hours:	Call in advance to ensure there will be a deputy available to show you the prison cells.
Amenities:	Prairie du Chien offers riverside parks, the Villa Louis Wisconsin Historic Site (https://villalouis.wisconsinhistory.org), and the Fort Crawford Museum (https://www.fortcrawfordmuseum.com).
Contact:	Crawford County Sheriff's Office, 224 N Beaumont Rd, Prairie du Chien, WI 53821. Phone: 608/326-8414. Website: www.crawfordcountysheriffwi.org/jail.html.

Cell with two metal bunks

FIRST PRESBYTERIAN CHURCH
RACINE COUNTY

Though inconclusive, evidence strongly suggests that Racine's First Presbyterian Church served as a stop on the Underground Railroad. Built for 500 in 1851, the church is the oldest sanctuary in the city.

Early church members included abolitionists, and individuals who owned slaves were denied membership. Several members were among the group who freed fugitive slave Joshua Glover from a Milwaukee jail, after Glover, who had sought asylum in Racine, was arrested under the Fugitive Slave Act.

Some fugitive slaves were rumored to have escaped to Canada via ships owned by local industrialist Henry Durand, another First Presbyterian member. Durand's mansion, now part of the Racine Masonic Center at 1012 Main St., featured a basement maze, also reportedly part of the Underground Railroad.

The clearest evidence linking the church to the Underground Railroad was uncovered during 1970s renovations when various artifacts were found in dirt crawl

spaces beneath the sanctuary. The items found—shoes, beef leg bones, hats, an 1845 Bible, newspapers, and small wooden chairs—did not suggest a dump or trash pit, but rather a living space. Today visitors can view an enlarged, cement-floored hallway where a tunnel-crawlspace once ran, as well as an old stone-walled furnace room.

Today's cement-floored hallway was once a tunnel-crawlspace.

The church basement also features a display of framed quilt blocks, depicting patterns that once pointed the way toward freedom. If a slave, for example, hung a "bear's paw" quilt in the plantation yard, it reportedly sent a message for fugitive slaves to use winding animal trails and avoid the main roads on their escape route north. A "bow-tie" quilt advised them to get married: Slaves were not permitted to marry, so a married African-American man and woman were less likely to be perceived as slaves.

You can learn more about the Underground Railroad in Racine by visiting the church. 716 College Ave., or the Racine Heritage Museum, 701 Main St. Phone ahead to arrange small group tours of the church. The museum features an exhibit, "This Train Is Bound for Glory: Racine County's Underground Railroad," which showcases a few artifacts from First Presbyterian Church. The museum also offers an adult education program on the Underground Railroad; in addition, watch its website for heritage walking tours that describe and pass by First Presbyterian Church.

Directions:	First Presbyterian Church, 716 College Ave., and the Racine Heritage Museum, 701 Main St., are both located in downtown Racine, within a few blocks of Lake Michigan. Main Street runs north and south, roughly paralleling the lakeshore; College Avenue parallels Main Street, two blocks to the west.
Seasons/ Hours:	Reservations required for tours of the church. Donations accepted. Racine Heritage Museum is open Tuesday through Friday, from 9 a.m. to 5 p.m.; Saturday, from 10 a.m. to 3 p.m.; and Sunday, from noon to 4 p.m. Free.
Amenities:	Other highlights of Racine's downtown and lakefront: Racine Art Museum, Racine Zoological Society, Wind Point Lighthouse, and S. C. Johnson Headquarters.
Contact	First Presbyterian Church phone: 262/632-1686; email: FirstPresRacine@wi.rr.com. Websites: www.firstpresracine.org and www.racineheritagemuseum.org.

FORT COMMUNITY CREDIT UNION
JEFFERSON COUNTY

Theories abound as to the original use of the tunnel that once ran beneath Main Street in Jefferson. The most often heard explanation related to the movement of illegal liquor during the Prohibition era. Whatever the reason, there's no denying the tunnel's existence, because visitors can still enter a few feet of it from the basement of the Fort Community Credit Union branch office. Though now blocked off, there is enough of the arched tunnel remaining to spark the obvious question: Why?

Cut-out roof of tunnel

From the credit union's first-floor entry area, you can see the exterior top of the tunnel, revealed as part of 2003 renovations. A portion of its roof has been removed, allowing natural light to illumine the passage, which has limestone walls on its east side and Cream City brick on the ceiling.

One place to search for answers is at the City Museum, two blocks away at 317 S. Main St. Genealogists desiring to research ancestors from the region can browse eighty family history scrapbooks. From February to December, the museum is open on Wednesday from 10 a.m. to noon and Sunday from 1 p.m. to 4 p.m. During the summer, it is also open Saturday from 10 a.m. to 1 p.m.

Author, near the blocked-off tunnel end (Photo: Mary Lou Santovec)

Directions:	The Jefferson branch office of Fort Community Credit Union is located downtown at 100 N. Main St. Jefferson is on U.S. 18 between Madison and Milwaukee. The building also houses a law office and the office of the Council for the Performing Arts.
Seasons/ Hours:	Access Monday through Friday, 9 a.m. to 5 p.m. Upon entering the building, take the elevator (or stairs) to the basement.
Length:	The accessible tunnel section is approximately fifty feet long.
Amenities:	Situated at the confluence of the Crawfish and Rock Rivers, Jefferson is noted for its historic downtown and regular schedule of spring to fall indoor and outdoor events.
Contact:	Fort Community Credit Union, 100 N. Main St., Jefferson, WI 53549. Phone: 920/674-7020. Website: https://www.fortcommunity.com/about-us/locations-hours.html.

IRVINE PARK
CHIPPEWA COUNTY

Do you long for a room with a view? Instead, how about a cave with a zoo? Chippewa Falls' Irvine Park contains both a municipal zoo and a cave, the latter appropriately next to the former bear den.

F.X. Schmitmayer, owner of Schmitmayer Brewing Company, purchased the small sandstone cave and seven acres along Pine Creek in 1871. He enlarged the cave, which contained a natural spring, and closed the side entrance. Next, he dug a shaft into the cave from above, so that barrels of beer could be lowered into the cool cave for aging. Today a Chippewa County Historical Society marker stands before the cave, commemorating Schmitmayer's brewery and later developments leading to the creation of the park.

After the Schmitmayer Brewing Company closed, William Irvine purchased the property along with adjoining acreage. Subsequently the fifty-three-acre parcel was developed as Irvine Park. The zoo began in 1909 with the bear den constructed near the cave. In 2005, a new 5,000-square-foot bear den opened. In addition to the bears, the zoo contains elk, deer, buffalo, ostriches, peacocks, and other animals. There's even a band shell, log house, 1903 schoolhouse, and the Rumbly Bridge. Erected in 1907 over Duncan Creek near the Park's rear entrance, it may be the only remaining metal truss bridge in Wisconsin originally designed as an ornamental park bridge.

Close by the Jacob Leinenkugel Brewing Company has operated on the same site in Chippewa Falls since 1867. It, too, used to store beer in a bluff cave behind the brewery operation. The Leinenkugel cave, however, is no longer accessible. The brewery constructed a building in front of the cave entrance as part of an expansion project.

Directions:	From U.S. 53, take State Highway 124 north. Continue on State Highway 124 until you see the Jacob Leinenkugel Brewing Company on the right. Turn left on Bridgewater Avenue, then drive to Bear Den Road and turn right onto Bear Den Road. Drive to the end of the road and park. The end of the road is closed to motor vehicles. Walk less than a half mile to the cave.
Seasons/ Hours:	Open daily from 7 a.m. to dusk. Free.
Length:	Cave is perhaps fifteen feet wide and extends approximately thirty feet into the hill.
Precautions:	Watch for poison ivy in the greenery across from the cave opening.
Amenities:	Playground equipment, shelters, picnic tables, restrooms.
Contact:	Chippewa Falls Parks, Recreation and Forestry Department, 30 W Central St., Chippewa Falls, WI 54729. Phone: 715/723-3890. http://www.chippewafalls-wi.gov/your-government/parks-recreation-forestry/irvine-park-zoo/zoo.

Irvine Park's enlarged sandstone cave

MILLER BREWING COMPANY
MILWAUKEE COUNTY

Before refrigeration, Wisconsin brewers used caves and cellars to keep their lager beer cool during the several-week aging process. While most are no longer publicly accessible, you can visit one of these historic cave storage facilities in Milwaukee as part of a Miller Brewery tour. Today this manmade cave houses historical exhibits—for example, brewery artifacts, filled sample bottles of competitors' beer and soda, miniature dioramas showing the brewing process, barrels, and cooperage tools.

Workers dug the cave in the 1850s—300 feet horizontally into the hillside, sixty-two feet beneath the top of the hill. Near the end of the cave, they created side tunnels for added space. The ceiling height ranges from eleven feet at the entrance to nineteen feet in the main room.

Before Miller Brewing Company installed refrigeration in 1906, it used the caverns to store up to 12,000 barrels of beer at a time, requiring more than 6,000 tons of ice each year.

After remaining closed for many years, parts of the tunnels reopened during the Cold War of the 1950s as a bomb shelter. Frederick C. Miller, grandson of founder Frederick J. Miller, renovated the caves, installing a slate floor and lining the walls and

*Historic Miller Caves with mural, silhouetted cooper (barrel-maker) in background
(Photo: Miller Brewing Company Visitor Center)*

arched ceiling with brown brick. Some sections of the tunnels were filled in. Finally in the late 1950s, the Miller Caves Museum was developed as part of a new tour program and continues to be a highlight of the tour today. You can also rent the caves for your next event; guest capacity is one hundred (standing) or fifty (seated).

The Miller Brewing Company tour also features a video history of the brewery; a visit to the brewhouse, packaging, and shipping areas; and, lastly, to the Bavarian-style Miller Inn (or the beer garden in summer) for product samples. Soda is also served.

Directions:	From I-94, exit at Thirty-fifth Street. Travel north about six blocks to West State Street. Turn left and look for the visitor center on the left.
Seasons/ Hours:	From Memorial Day weekend through Labor Day weekend tours typically run every half hour between 10 a.m. and 6 p.m., Monday through Friday; 10 a.m. and 6:30 p.m. Saturday, and 10 am to 3:30 p.m. on Sunday. From Labor Day weekend to Memorial Day weekend, tours end one hour earlier Monday through Saturday; closed on Sunday. See website or call for updated daily tour times, holiday schedules, special needs, and group reservations. Free.
Length:	Tour takes about one hour. Caves Museum extends about 300 feet into the hillside.
Precautions:	No strollers permitted.
Amenities:	Gift shop sells branded clothing and other items. And, of course, Milwaukee offers a multitude of cultural, shopping, and dining opportunities.
Contact:	Miller Brewing Company Visitor Center, 4251 W. State St., Milwaukee, WI 53208. Phone: 414/931-BEER (2337) or 800/944-LITE (5483). Website: https://www.millercoors.com/breweries/miller-brewing-company/tours/tour-information. Also see Bobby Tanzilo's *On Milwaukee* series on Urban Spelunking: https://onmilwaukee.com/buzz/articles/urban-spelunking-miller-caves.html.

MILTON HOUSE
ROCK COUNTY

The Milton House tunnel is a certified segment of the Underground Railroad in Wisconsin and one of the few documented segments to actually run underground. Using grout, Joseph Goodrich constructed the hexagonal stagecoach inn in 1844. The tunnel connects the Milton House to a nearby log cabin built in 1837.

A member of the Seventh Day Baptist church and the Whig political party, Goodrich was also an abolitionist, hiding and aiding fugitive slaves before the Civil War. Although there were many other abolitionists in the area, Goodrich operated a public tavern and could not always trust his customers to share his antislavery views. Fugitives generally stayed in the basement of the Milton House, resting and recuperating before undertaking the next stage of their journey. If there was ever a need for a speedy escape, they exited through a low (three-to-five-foot high) dirt tunnel leading to a ladder and trapdoor in the floor of the cabin. From there, they could travel along several lakes and streams eventually arriving at Lake Koshkonong; and from there, traveling to Fort Atkinson or other northerly destinations.

Milton House, stagecoach inn constructed in 1844

The narrow tunnel has been enlarged so that visitors can stand up in it. A cement floor, walls, and lighting have also been added, and a stairway has replaced the ladder to the cabin. Yet the tunnel retains a stark simplicity, a reminder that its purpose was not comfort or ease, but freedom and survival.

The tunnel begins near a corner of the basement where fugitive slaves probably hid. If an alarm sounded the fugitives would be on their way in seconds. Entering the tunnel, you imagine hearing the hastening feet, the muffled sounds of people crouching and hurrying through the dark, dirt passage. Reaching the other end, they would quickly climb the ladder up the dirt shaft. Rugs and loose floorboards were pushed aside, and the fugitives emerged into the small cabin, which they immediately left, carrying their belongings with them.

You climb the stairs slowly, more than a hundred and fifty years after the slaves, and wonder whether you can really understand what they felt and experienced. Today the cabin is largely bare, but the rough stone fireplace still dominates the single room as it did in the mid-nineteenth century.

The tour also includes a blacksmith shop, buggy house, smokehouse, and, of course, the upper levels of the Milton House. But what you remember most is the tunnel, and maybe that rugged rock fireplace.

Directions:	From I-90, follow State Highway 26 to Milton. The museum is State Highway 26 just north of its intersection with State Highway 59.
Seasons/ Hours:	Memorial Day through Labor Day, open daily, 10 a.m. to 4 p.m.; Labor Day to Memorial Day, Tuesday through Friday, 1 p.m. to 4 p.m. Or, call to schedule a private tour. Fee.
Length:	Complete tour takes one hour.
Precautions:	Tour includes several stairways.
Amenities:	Milton House Museum contains a gift shop and the town offers antiques shops, restaurants, and other attractions.
Contact	Milton House Museum, 18 S. Janesville St., Milton, WI 53563. Phone: 608/868-7772. Website: http://www.miltonhouse.org.

OSHKOSH DOWN UNDER
WINNEBAGO COUNTY

After significant research, Julie Krysiak Johnson published her book, *Oshkosh Down Under: Basement Businesses and the Tunnel from the Hotel Athearn to the Grand Opera House*, in 2002. Relying on old newspaper files, the 1903 Sanborn Fire Insurance Map, and eye-witness accounts, she investigated the existence of a tunnel running from the Athearn Hotel (razed in 1964) to the renovated, 1883 Grand Opera House. While suggestive, the evidence is not quite conclusive. And yet, wouldn't it be convenient for both performers and audience members to have had a sheltered walkway from the hotel to the opera house?

Today the tunnel remains an oft-told story, particularly around Halloween each year. "The story of the tunnel between [the] Grand and the Athearn Hotel is one we tell regularly—but I usually do so with a caveat," said Joseph Ferlo, Oshkosh Opera House

Foundation president and CEO. "While there is evidence of basement shops in the Opera House, there is no physical evidence of the opening of a tunnel. For every person who calls it a myth, there is someone whose grandfather had used it."

Oshkosh: lower level doorway

What is certain is the existence of various businesses at basement level in the opera house and many downtown Oshkosh buildings. Krysiak Johnson located substantial documentation about them, for example, city directory listings and advertisements. Exterior stairwells descending to these lower-level businesses and prismatic glass windows set into the sidewalks to provide light below once marked their existence in Oshkosh and no doubt other eastern Wisconsin cities.

PIER NATURAL BRIDGE COUNTY PARK
RICHLAND COUNTY

The underground attractions at the ten-acre Pier Park are both natural and manmade. First, the West Branch of the Pine River cuts through a natural bridge in a sixty-foot sandstone bluff, near its mouth into the main branch of the river. Second, men have cut a tunnel through the bluff so that visitors can walk through it and view the bridge from both sides without swimming. At first glace, you might think that you could do a canoe limbo underneath the natural passage, but sometimes the water level is too high and the clearance too low.

In the first half of the twentieth century William Francis Pier donated the land for the park in memory of his father, William Henry Pier. But the parcel has a much longer history. According to a Wisconsin Historical Marker, General Henry Atkinson camped at the site on the night of July 29, 1832 during the Black Hawk War. In previous centuries Native Americans used the rock shelter beneath a sandstone overhang just south of the rock bridge.

Tunnel at Pier Natural Bridge County Park

Pier Park is a great spot for a picnic or a short break from traveling. A playground can help the kids release built-up energy, and the short hike up the stairs to the top of the bluff offers a pleasant way to stretch your legs. Covered in evergreen trees and shrubs, the top provides a peaceful view of the Pine River. After a brief meditation, you're prepped to tackle the next stage of a trip or ready for a return to the weekday work schedule.

Or, for a longer respite, the park offers a few campsites (tent only).

Directions:	Take State Highway 80 north of Richland Center. Pier Park is on the west side of the highway between Hub City and Rockbridge.
Seasons/ Hours:	Open year-round. Free.
Length:	The tunnel is more than fifty feet long.
Precautions:	Watch for poison ivy in the greenery across from the cave opening.
Amenities:	Six campsites (tent only), fishing, picnicking, playground, toilets, limited hiking to top of bluff. Adjacent to the park, Natural Bridge Store offers park camping registrations, groceries, camping supplies, fishing licenses, and more (https://www.facebook.com/NaturalBridgeStore/).
Contact:	Richland County Parks Commission, 26136 Executive Ln., Ste. C, Richland Center, WI 53581-1398. Phone: 608/647-2100. Website: https://parkscommission.co.richland.wi.us/county-parks/pier-natural-bridge-park.

Potosi Brewery
Grant County

Today run by a nonprofit foundation, Potosi Brewery operated as a business from 1852 to 1972. A series of skilled brewmasters led the production of quality beer, distributing, for example, 1,250 barrels in the mid-1870s and 6,500 barrels in 1908. The brewery produced "near" beer during Prohibition and focused on quality to survive in later years. But by the 1970s, increased competition from national breweries and the retirement of longtime owners led to the decision to close the business.

Gary David purchased the by then dilapidated facility in 1995 and soon enlisted help from local residents; the Potosi Brewery Foundation formed in 2000. A year later the property was transferred to the foundation, and the brewery reopened in 2008 after a $7.5 million restoration. The historic Main Street building is also home to the

The Cave showcases historic artifacts at Potosi Brewery.

National Brewery Museum, a brewpub, beer garden, gift shop, Great River Road Interpretive Center—and The Cave. Backing into the bluff behind the brewery, the Cave once served as beer storage but today contains wooden barrels and other artifacts of nineteenth-century brewing.

When the first Potosi brewmaster selected a site for his brewery, he located it at the spot where a clear stream gushed from the base of a bluff, offering an abundant supply of spring water. The site is not far from the old St. John Mine, a lead mine that began in Snake Cave, another opening higher in the bluff face. Willis St. John discovered veins of lead in the cave walls and floor and started this mine about 1825. After operating it for more than twenty years, St. John sold this mine to Henry Massy and Nelson Dewey, Wisconsin's first governor. Until a few years ago, lucky visitors could tour this mine, but it closed following the retirement of Harry Henderson, who operated the mine after a career as a professor at the University of Wisconsin-Platteville and American University in Beirut, Lebanon.

Directions:	Potosi is located west of Platteville on State Hwy. 133, which is also Main Street.
Seasons/ Hours:	Check website for tour days and times; limited tours only on weekends, from January through March. Fee includes beer and gifts, including a year-long pass to the National Brewery Museum and Library.
Amenities:	For a small town, Potosi has a lot going for it. Check out the Great River Road Museum of Contemporary Art, Whispering Bluffs Winery, the Old Irish Cemetery, and not far out of town, the Great River Recreation Area.
Contact:	Potosi Brewery, 209 South Main St., Potosi, WI 53820. Phone: 608/763-4002. Website: www.potosibrewery.com

TOWER HILL STATE PARK
IOWA COUNTY

A tunnel, tower, and vertical shaft in the sandstone bluff at Tower Hill State Park stand as a monument to the perseverance of two men who tunneled 120 feet down and ninety feet horizontally using nothing more than picks and shovels and crowbars. Their motivation was the creation of a shot tower to produce lead shot for use in nineteenth-century firearms. Workers produced shot at the tower from 1831 to 1861, pouring molten lead into a special ladle-strainer. As the lead fell in droplets through the shaft, it cooled into spherical shapes that hardened when they plunged into a pool of water at the bottom of the shaft. Workers removed this lead shot through the horizontal tunnel running from the base of the shaft to the south bank of the Wisconsin River. They then shipped the ammunition upstream to Green Bay and out to the East Coast and also possibly downstream to the Mississippi. Now you can view the operation from displays in the rebuilt smelter house at the top of the shaft.

The shot tower stands as the only remnant of the 1830s town of Helena (pronounced to rhyme with Galena), which sprouted around the tower and grew to include a lumberyard, post office, and cooper shop, among other businesses. But in 1857 the railroad arrived. The new track ran a few miles north of town, dooming it as a viable economic center. Eventually the site was abandoned and the buildings destroyed. Many of their foundations are now underwater, covered by the shifting course of the Wisconsin River.

In its next reincarnation, the Tower Hill site became a church camp and retreat operated by a Unitarian minister named Jenkin Lloyd Jones, uncle of Frank Lloyd Wright. In 1922, Jones's widow, Edith, sold the property for $1 to the state for the development of the park. The pavilion the minister built now serves as a shelter you can

This tunnel runs from the base of the shot tower shaft to exit the bluff near the Wisconsin River.

reserve for picnics and other gatherings. It you happen to stumble over limestone foundations hidden in the woods, you have found other remains left by the church camp.

More recently storms and erosion have impacted the seventy-seven-acre park, and one trail segment leading to the tunnel opening on Mill Creek has been closed. Atop the bluff, the wood tower extends outward from the bluff edge; its base strikes the sloping bluff face, where the shaft begins. The shaft descends through the sandstone to the tunnel, which is on a level with the banks of Mill Creek and the Wisconsin River. A short trail leads from the top of the tower to the base of the wooden segment and ends—no longer continuing to the bank of the creek. To reach the tunnel entrance at the creek, take the trail beginning at the rear of campsite number fourteen or the longer trail beyond the shelter and past the service road. Watch your steps: Several park trails are bordered with poison ivy, and the trail from the top of the tower to the top of the dug shaft is steep and rugged.

While the shot tower is the main attraction of the seventy-acre park, it also serves as a popular picnic spot for canoeists, as well as drive-in visitors. Fifteen rustic campsites provide overnight respite.

There is another restored shot tower in the lead region, however, it is completely aboveground. The tapered, square shot tower in Dubuque, Iowa, stands about 120 feet above the current ground level. The exterior base measures about nineteen square feet, while the top measures a little more than twelve square feet. The interior square shaft is roughly thirteen square feet. Dubuque's tower is located at 600 E. Commercial Street.

Directions:	From Madison, drive west on U.S. 14. About five miles past Arena, turn left on County Highway C and drive a mile and a half to the park entrance on your right.
Seasons/ Hours:	Open year-round, 6 a.m. to 11 p.m. Although the main gate is closed from Columbus Day to mid-May, you can park at the entrance and walk in. Vehicle admission sticker required.
Length:	Tunnel is ninety feet long; the vertical shaft is 120 feet deep.
Precautions:	Hiking trail from campsite fourteen on the top of the bluff to the tunnel on the riverbank is fairly rough. Watch for poison ivy along the trails.
Amenities:	Rustic camping (eleven sites), fishing, hiking, picnicking, boat launch on Mill Creek. American Players Theater, which performs Shakespeare and other classic plays, and the Frank Lloyd Wright Visitor Center are nearby on County Highway C.
Contact:	Tower Hill State Park, 5808 County Highway C, Spring Green, WI 53588. Phone: 608/588-2116. Website: http://dnr.wi.gov/topic/parks/name/towerhill/.

VON STIEHL WINERY
KEWAUNEE COUNTY

Constructed in the mid-nineteenth century as the Ahnapee Brewing Company, this historic Algoma building now houses the von Stiehl Winery. The brewery produced about 500 barrels of beer annually, aging it in underground tunnels, until 1886 when a blight of Wisconsin's hops crop led to the company's demise. The building was subsequently used by different firms as a warehouse and to produce fly nets for horses and gas-powered washing machines.

By the 1960s the building had fallen into disrepair when it was rescued by Dr. Charles Von Stiehl, who restored it and created Wisconsin's first licensed winery, producing Door County cherry and apple wines for fourteen years. He sold the business in 1981 to Bill and Sandy Schmiling, who retained the Von Stiehl Winery name and added grape, cranberry, and other fruit wines to the company's offerings. Today the Schmilling's sons, Aric and Brad, run the winery.

They moved all production to a new facility in 2011, but you can still see the old limestone tunnels on a tour of the winery. Come to learn about the region's German and Belgian history—and to sample a variety of the winery's products.

Directions:	Located two blocks off of State Highway 42 on the Ahnapee River in downtown Algoma. Watch for signs.
Seasons/ Hours:	From May through October, tours begin at 9:30 a.m., 10:30 a.m., 11:30 a.m., 1 p.m., 2 p.m., 3 p.m., and 4 p.m. From November through April, tours are offered on Saturdays at 10:30 a.m. and 1:30 p.m. VIP tours are offered from January through April at 1 p.m. on Fridays— call for reservations. Note: There are stairs involved in the tours during the winter months. Fee.
Length:	Tour takes about two hours.
Amenities:	Picnic area and walkway with a view of the Lake Michigan harbor. Gift shop.
Contact:	Von Stiehl Winery, 115 Navarino St., Algoma, WI 54201. Phone: 920/487-5208. Website: https://vonstiehl.com/.

WALKER HOUSE
IOWA COUNTY

Dating to the mid-nineteenth century, the Walker House has had multiple additions over the years yet retains the feel and comforts of a nineteenth-century inn. William Walker emigrated from Ireland in 1839 and worked as a teamster, carrying lead as far as Milwaukee, before purchasing two lots on the south end of town and constructing an inn. Its location proved fortuitous when the railroad came through Mineral Point, just a long stone's throw from his property, in 1857.

Built of stone, the Walker House, which is on the National Register of Historic Places, contains forty-two rooms and covers almost 16,000 square feet. Considering its beamed ceilings, narrow stairways, and other signs of obvious age, perhaps the ghost stories circulating through its long history were bound to be created, whether real or imagined.

Yet there's no question about the reality of two "caves" carved into the rock of the hillside backing the building. While current Walker House staff refer to these rooms extending from the dining room as caves, they more likely once served as root cellars. Of course, a few folks believe the caves were originally badger huts housing early lead miners, but the appearance of these stone rooms is certainly more suggestive of root cellars. Today they serve as added dining alcoves.

Similar root cellars can be found at other Mineral Point locations, for example, off the patio of Popolo Pizzeria, 20 Commerce St., and at the Pendarvis Wisconsin Historic Site. There, a similar, arched, stone ceilinged root cellar was carved into the bluff at the rear of Polperro House.

One of two Walker House "caves" extending from the dining room

Directions:	From Business U.S. Hwy. 151, turn left onto Commerce Street. Turn left again onto State Hwy. 23/39 and then take the first right onto Water Street. The Walker House will be on the left.
Amenities:	Besides Pendarvis (https://pendarvis.wisconsinhistory.org), nearby attractions include Shake Rag Center for the Arts (www.shakeragalley.com), and many restaurants, shops, and art galleries.
Contact:	The Walker House, 1 Water St, Mineral Point, WI 53565. Phone: 608/553-0728. Website: http://thewalkerhouse.org.

WOLLERSHEIM WINERY
DANE COUNTY

The small cave dug into the hillside at Wollersheim Winery dates to the 1840s, when Hungarian Count Agoston Haraszthy selected the slopes across the Wisconsin River from Prairie du Sac for his vineyards. He dug the cave to store the aging wine. After several years of winter damage to his young vineyards, however, Haraszthy left his Wisconsin River valley experiment in 1849, to follow the gold rush to California, where he eventually became known as the founder of that state's wine industry.

Wollersheim Winery's hand-dug cave dates to the 1840s.

A German immigrant, Peter Kehl, took over the young vineyard, developing it and adding the stone buildings of the winery during the Civil War. For a time, he reportedly lived in the small cave, while working on building additional structures. To combat the problem of Wisconsin's cold winters, Kehl buried some of his vines every year, and under his management, the grapes and the winery grew. Kehl's son Jacob continued to develop both the vineyards and the winery after Peter's death, selling barrels of wine as far away as Maine. After Jacob's death in 1899, however, the family converted the land to more traditional farming.

Robert and JoAnn Wollersheim purchased the property in 1972, reestablishing the vineyards and the winery. The Wollersheims continued to develop this property and their business with the assistance of French winemaker Philippe Coquard, who eventually married Robert and JoAnn's daughter, Julie. Many family members are involved in the enterprise, which has grown tremendously over the decades. In 1990 the Wollersheims purchased Cedarburg's Cedar Creek Winery. Thirty years later, Wollersheim Winery received a distillery license and commenced making brandy.

Today you can visit the small manmade cave during regular winery hours. Adults can also sample some of the winery's products.

Directions:	On U.S. 12, seventeen miles north of Middleton and a quarter mile south of Sauk City, turn east on State Highway 188. Drive two miles; the winery will be on your right.
Seasons/ Hours:	Open daily 10 a.m. to 5 p.m. Free.
Length:	Cave is approximately fifty feet long; a tour takes forty-five minutes.
Amenities:	Outdoor wine garden, gift shop, restrooms. Distillery tours also available.
Contact:	Wollersheim Winery and Distillery, 7876 State Hwy. 188, P.O. Box 87, Prairie du Sac, WI 53578. Phone: 800/847-9463. Website: http://www.wollersheim.com/.

CLIFFSIDE CAVES
CLAYTON COUNTY, IOWA

Backed up against the Mississippi River bluffs, McGregor, Iowa, made the most of its geography. In the mid-nineteenth century, its early citizens dug caves into the bluffs backing the main streets for use as cool, dry storage areas. Walking about town, you still can see some of these manmade caves in the sides of the bluffs.

For instance, several are visible behind the large building at 214 A Street. Built in 1850 to house McGregor's city hall, it has since housed various businesses. Different owners have refurbished, renovated, and generally updated the unique building. One owner added the fire escape above the courtyard, which reputedly came from the old Jackson School in Cedar Rapids, which the Wright Brothers, Grant Wood, and Mamie Eisenhower all attended, according to the owner.

Walking west, you will soon pass Bluffside Gardens. If you continue west of the luxurious gardens, you will come to another small cave in the bluff, but you won't want to enter it. A sign posted near the opening warns: "Rattlesnakes"!

Careful—snakes alive!

Time to return to your car.

Two miles north, in Marquette, other openings in the bluff appear as black gouges along Iowa State Highway 76/Business U.S. 18. Watch for these caves in the bluff across the road from the Casino Queen on Anti Monopoly Street. If you're in the mood for a different kind of adventure, you may want to try your luck at the casino or check out the dining and shopping opportunities in this old Mississippi River town.

Directions:	Cliffside caves are visible as you walk the streets of downtown McGregor, Iowa. Examples are located behind 214 A Street.
Seasons/ Hours:	Caves are visible year-round.
Length:	Several caves extend twenty feet into the hillside.
Amenities:	Outdoor wine garden, gift shop, restrooms. Distillery tours also available.
Contact:	McGregor and Marquette Chamber of Commerce, 146 Main St., McGregor, IA 52157. Phone: 800/896-0910 or 319/873-2186. Website: http://www.mcgreg-marq.org/

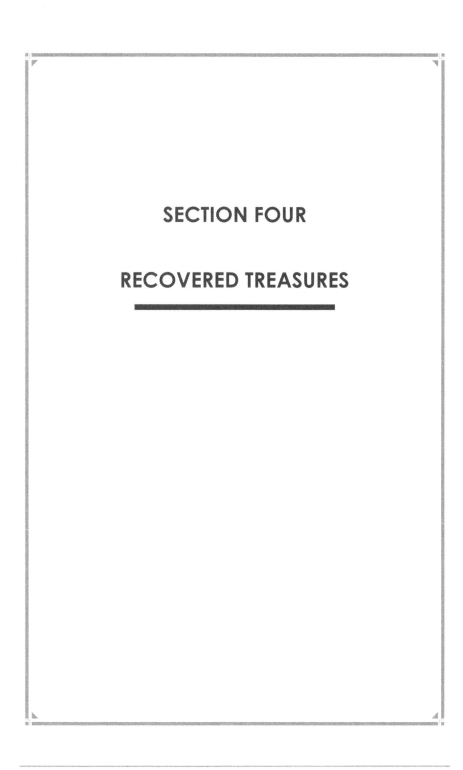

SECTION FOUR

RECOVERED TREASURES

MID-CONTINENT RAILWAY

The tracks owned by the Mid-Continent Railway Museum in North Freedom were constructed in 1903 as a feeder line to serve the iron mines near Quartzite Lake and La Rue, a Baraboo Hills community about four miles south of North Freedom. The tracks ended in North Freedom at the Chicago & Northwestern Railroad line and depot. The restored C&NW depot now houses the museum.

You can still experience the steam train trip to La Rue in one of several restored passenger cars. The trains run three times daily from June to September and on weekends only during the latter part of May and from September to the third week of October. Special excursions are scheduled several times a year, for instance, the Snow Train in February, the Stars and Stripes Special in June/July, the Autumn Color Train and Pumpkin Special in October, and the Santa Express in December. The railway offers onboard dining options (pizza barbeque, dinner, beer, wine) on select dates.

Mid-Continent is an outdoor living history museum and operating railroad that preserve the small-town, short-line, steam-powered railroading experience. Efforts include maintaining the depot museum and restoring steam locomotives and passenger cars.

To reach the museum, take State Highway 136 west of Baraboo for about four miles to County PF. Turn left (south) to North Freedom. At the four-way stop, go straight onto West Walnut Street, which becomes Museum Road. To learn more, call 608/522-4261 or visit www.midcontinent.org.

You might think the title of this book would pretty much cover any type of underground space you could imagine. Yet, there are interesting underground structures that seem to belong here, without fitting precisely into the three major categories of caves, mines, or tunnels. This section presents these miscellaneous sites and lists museums offering replicas of underground structures and related educational exhibits.

While a few of the sites described in this section at first might appear to readily fit into an earlier section, most lack historic significance and, to some degree, the historic appearance of an old railroad tunnel, limestone kiln, or other nineteenth-century subterranean structure. In fact, several sites are not underground at all. Yet, all these sites seemed closely enough related to Wisconsin's underground structures, their mystique and history, to warrant mention here. A visit to any of them can help put you in touch with a Wisconsin based as much on rocks and minerals as on dairying, hunting, and fishing.

ROCHE-A-CRI STATE PARK
ADAMS COUNTY

Although it does not offer an underground experience, Roche-A-Cri State Park draws many geology and archaeology students—not to mention hikers, cross-country skiers, picnickers, and other outdoor enthusiasts. The name "Roche-A-Cri" is French and means "crevice in the rock." Roche-A-Cri Mound, towers 300 feet above the surrounding plains and features a vertical cleft on its south side. The park offers long-range views from the top of the mound, as well as a close look at ancient rock art near its base. Originally an island in Glacial Lake Wisconsin, the sandstone butte helps visitors imagine what this region looked like 15,000 or so years ago.

Several types of rock art are visible from an accessible observation ramp at the base of the mound's south side. Interpretative signs describe the pictographs (paintings) and crow feet petroglyphs (carvings), which resemble birds' feet and may date to 900 A.D. or earlier. More recent graffiti on the wall was left by some of Adam County's earliest European settlers and dates from 1847. According to 1851 survey notes, rock art was also found in a small cave at the butte.

Graffiti has not been the only threat to the ancient rock art. Erosion of the bluff face by wind and rain continues, and the Wisconsin Department of Natural Resources has taken several steps to protect the ancient paintings and carvings, as well as the mound itself. Concern over the potential for vandalism combined with the dangers of climbing the crumbly sandstone cliffs prompted the DNR to ban climbing the sides of the mound and using the top.

A stairway up the northwest side of the butte leads to the top of Roche-A-Cri Mound. Interpretative signs detail significant features of the rock art and other park features.

At least one previous guidebook has noted the presence of a small cave containing rock art on Roche-A-Cri. Preservation efforts, however, made this cave off limits to visitors today.

Directions:	Main park entrance is on State Highway 13, approximately one and a half miles north of Friendship. A winter parking area is on Czech Avenue, which intersects State Highway 13 about a quarter mile south of the main entrance.
Seasons/ Hours:	Open year-round, from 6 a.m. to 11 p.m., although the main entrance and office are closed from November 1 through April 30. The stairway to the top of the mound is open from 6 a.m. to sunset. Vehicle admission sticker required.
Precautions:	The stairway hike to the top of the mound can be a challenge. An accessible shelter located near the beginning of the stairway contains a kiosk with educational displays. Also accessible are several trails, a campsite, and the series of interpretative panels at the rock art site on the south side of the mound.
Amenities:	Hiking, picnicking, camping, fishing, playground, toilets, cross-country skiing, snowshoeing, and hunting and trapping.
Contact:	Roche-A-Cri State Park, 1767 State Highway 13, Friendship, WI 53934. Phone: 608/339-6881. Phone: 608/339-6881 (summer) or 608/565-2789 (off-season). Website: http://dnr.wi.gov/topic/parks/name/ rocheacri/.

WISCONSIN ROCK ART

Wisconsin has one of the most concentrated areas of early rock art in the eastern United States, with well over 100 known sites. Although the majority are located in the caves and rock shelters of the Driftless area, examples can be found scattered throughout the state. Many sites are found in outcroppings of St. Peters sandstone. Sometimes the images applied to or carved into the rock walls and faces are unknown to the landowners or not understood to be ancient rock art. A prehistoric painting can appear to be modern graffiti or some quirk of nature.

Despite the large number of sites, most are generally unpublicized, for fear of vandalism. This concern is, unfortunately, warranted. Several sites have incurred significant damage from vandals, including at least one incident in which would-be thieves ruined invaluable art while attempting to cut it out of a rock wall.

As a result, there are limited ways to view Wisconsin's rock art. In addition to a visit to Roche-A-Cri State Park, you may want to check out these resources, which include information, events, and special opportunities related to Wisconsin's effigy mounds and rock art sites:

- Cultural Landscape Legacies, Inc., is a nonprofit with a mission of educating, protecting, and preserving the cultural heritage of the indigenous people who left their legacy on the landscape of the Upper Midwest. Website: www.clli.org.

- The Mississippi Valley Archaeology Center at the University of Wisconsin-La Crosse researches, preserves, and teaches about the archaeological resources of the Upper Mississippi River region. Website: http://mvac.uwlax.edu.

- Former Wisconsin State Archaeologist Robert Birmingham authored a second edition of his classic book, *Indian Mounds of Wisconsin*, in 2017.

- *Hidden Thunder: Rock Art of the Upper Midwest*, published in 2016, is a collaboration of watercolor artist Geri Schrab and archaeologist Robert "Ernie" Boszhardt.

MUSEUMS AND UNDERGROUND EXHIBITS

Caught up in the joy of traversing a cliff path on a sunny day or in the fascination of exploring a dark mine passage, it's easy to forget that several Wisconsin museums offer educational exhibits that can deepen our understanding of trips underground. A number of local museums display the artifacts associated with mines or caves in their immediate vicinities, and several major museums have erected replicas of underground structures as part of their educational missions.

CROSSROADS AT BIG CREEK
DOOR COUNTY

Crossroads at Big Creek is a 200-acre scientific, historical, and environmental preserve. Its John and Helen Collins Learning Center provides accessible space for classes and lectures, lab research, and three exhibits. The eight-two-seat lecture hall provides multimedia options for public, school, and organizational presentations. During the

summer, researchers from the University of Wisconsin-Oshkosh work with the Door County Public Health Department and Door County Soil and Water and use the Crossroads lab to test the water of area beaches in Lake Michigan and the Bay of Green Bay.

With assistance from Meissner Landscaping, Inc. and advice from Gary Soule, cave archivist and historian, muralist Patty Clark created the Escarpment Display within the

Muralist Patty Clark showcased the Niagara Escarpment.

Escarpment Display realistic down to the boots!

learning center in 2010, the Year of the Escarpment. The exhibit depicts Door County caves and other features of the Niagara Escarpment—right down to the caver seen descending through a fissure in the rock above your head.

Clark also created the Great Lakes Ecosystem Display and the Wisconsin Wildlife Exhibit on different levels of the learning center. Both allow visitors to get a true sense of Northeast Wisconsin's ecology.

Throughout the year, Crossroads offers a multitude of opportunities for singles, families, and organizations to experience their outdoor environment. An outdoor "living room" for the area, people come to hike, participate in garden workshops, help with Earth Day activities, and participate in the life of the preserve in myriad other ways.

Directions:	From Green Bay, follow State Hwy. 57 north to Sturgeon Bay and turn right on Michigan Street.
Seasons/ Hours:	Learning center open daily; hours vary with the seasons—see website. Trails generally open daily year round.
Contact:	Crossroads at Big Creek, 2041 Michigan St, Sturgeon Bay, WI 54235. Phone: 920/746-5895 Website: http://www.crossroadsatbigcreek.com.

DOOR COUNTY HISTORICAL MUSEUM

One reason the *Chicago Tribune* called the Door County Historical Museum the "best small museum in the Midwest" likely related to its wildlife diorama, created by Mike Orthober, an award-winning artist and taxidermist. The four-season display presents over 100 birds, a white-tailed deer, badger, and fisher in realistic outdoor settings. A bear lumbers down toward a cave in a limestone escarpment and an observant raccoon eyes the surroundings.

A section of Mike Orthober's wildlife diorama

The museum's replica fire station is equally impressive with three restored trucks and related artifacts. In this same area of the museum, you can sit in a 1920 Oldsmobile and view a horse-drawn hearse. Other displays highlight Door County orchards, fish boils, folk art, village street scenes, and agricultural equipment.

From May 1 through October 31, the museum is open daily, 10 a.m. to 4:30 p.m. Contact: Door County Historical Museum, 18 N. 4th Ave., Sturgeon Bay, WI 54235. Phone: 920/743-5809. Website: http://map.co.door.wi.us/museum.

EARTHAVEN MUSEUM
OCONTO COUNTY

The nonprofit Earthaven Museum aims to foster appreciation for the earth sciences among all age groups. Its collections of more than 10,000 specimens educates all ages about the types, origins, and uses of minerals, gemstones, fossils, and meteorites.

Volunteers and staff provide offsite presentations for schools and other groups, as well as organized field trips. Participants can dig for minerals and fossils or pan for diamonds, gold, or garnets.

Directions:	Located northwest of Green Bay and northeast of Shawano. Fifield Road is off of State Hwy. 22 in Gillett.
Seasons/ Hours:	Usual hours are 9 a.m. to 4 p.m., Tuesday through Friday; 10 a.m. to 4 p.m. on Saturday; and 1 p.m. to 4 p.m. on Sunday. Call ahead to ensure staff is present and not out collecting or presenting. Closed on Mondays, Thanksgiving, Christmas Eve, Christmas Day, and New Year's Day. Free.
Contact:	Earthaven Museum, 7599 Fifield Rd, Gillett, WI 54124. Phone: 920/855-6132. Website: http://earthavenmuseum.org.

MILWAUKEE PUBLIC MUSEUM
MILWAUKEE COUNTY

Officially chartered in 1882, the Milwaukee Public Museum traces its beginnings to 1851 and the founding of the German-English Academy, which encouraged students to collect organic, geological, and archaeological specimens. Today the world-class museum contains more than four million specimens and 150,000 square feet of permanent and temporary exhibit space.

The museum's ongoing, first-floor exhibit, The Third Planet, enables you to journey through millions of years of Wisconsin's past in an hour or two. This walk through the state's geologic times explains how Wisconsin's surface and subsurface have been shaped, tempered, and reshaped over millions of years.

Southeastern Wisconsin's geologic past is reconstructed in the Silurian reef diorama, depicting how this area would have appeared over 400 million years ago when it was covered by a shallow sea. Nearby a massive replica of a mile-thick glacier mimics the eastern Wisconsin landscape of 12,000 years ago. Inside the walk-through glacier, you can rest on a rock and view videos on the glacier's advance and retreat in Pleistocene times.

As part of the same Third Planet exhibit, you can tour a solution cave replica, filled with displays depicting the development of this type of cave, common in the unglaciated southwestern quadrant of Wisconsin. In other sections, you can learn about the formation of minerals, volcanoes, earthquakes and plate tectonics—or the movement of the plates that make up the earth's crust. Plate tectonics and drifting continents have immensely impacted the evolution of life on earth.

For children and adults fascinated by dinosaurs, there's also an incredible array of fossils and dioramas highlighting the age when the enormous animals trod the area we now know as Wisconsin.

Exhibits throughout the museum explore how humans have interacted with their planet in other times and places. For instance, you can experience equatorial Africa, Asia, the Pacific Islands, and even learn how people lived above the Arctic Circle. This last exhibit features an Inuit woman preparing a meal inside a full-sized replica of an igloo. Closer to home in terms of time and distance, you also may want to explore the Streets of Old Milwaukee or Wisconsin Woodlands exhibits.

Directions:	From the North, go south on I-43. Take the Highland Ave. exit ramp. Turn left onto State St. Turn right on James Lovell St. Parking structure will be on your right. From the South, go north on I-94/43. Take Exit 72A toward Michigan St./10th St. Continue straight on 10th street. Turn right onto Wells St. Turn left onto James Lovell St. Parking structure will be on your left. From the West, go east on I-94. Take Exit 1H James Lovell St. Veer left onto James Lovell St. Drive north three blocks. Parking structure will be on your left.
Seasons/ Hours:	Open daily, except for July 4th, Thanksgiving, and Christmas, from 10 a.m. to 5 p.m., Monday through Friday; 9 a.m. to 5 p.m., Saturday; and 11 a.m. to 5 p.m., Sunday. Check website for occasionally early closing dates. Café hours are 11 a.m. to 2 p.m. daily; coffee kiosk hours vary. Fee.
Length:	The solution cave is about fifteen feet long; the glacier ice cave is about thirty feet long.
Precautions:	Parking is available in nearby municipal lots, including MacArthur Square Parking structure, which offers a direct, accessible entrance to the museum. Metered street parking is available on many downtown streets and is free on Sunday.
Amenities:	Spending an entire day at the museum is easy to do, with many excellent exhibits to explore—including the Rain Forest, Streets of Old Milwaukee, and a European Village. For an additional fee, you also can view various programs in the National Geographic Dome Theater or Daniel M. Soref Planetarium. There's also a café, coffee kiosk, and gift shop featuring items from around the globe. Check the website for periodic lectures, traveling exhibits, and other programs.
Contact:	Milwaukee Public Museum, 800 W. Wells St., Milwaukee, WI 53233. Phone: 414/278-2751. Website: www.mpm.edu.

DORCHESTER CAVE DISPLAY

Just knowing it's there is sometimes enough. Though Dorchester Cave is closed to the public, it is a type of cave unique in Door County and you can find a display telling the story of its discovery in 1972.

Lying hidden beneath Sturgeon Bay's original hospital, the cave was discovered during blasting to construct the basement of the Dorchester Nursing Home at the old hospital site on North Seventh Avenue. Wisconsin Speleological Society members, John Kellner and Gary Soule rushed to the site. A large rock was moved that blocked one of the two exposed passageways, Soule recalled. "We then pushed forward into the cave, discovering even walking height passage! I named [the passage] "Pennings Hall" after the owner of the property, John Pennings." Soule sketched a map of the cave and convinced Pennings to "save it from being sealed up forever."

Fifty-five feet of the cave was removed during construction, but 340 feet was preserved behind a locked basement door. It contains many non-weathered fossils, chain corrals, and layers of more resistant chert. Soule created a poster display documenting the cave and its discovery, located in the hallway leading to the closed entrance.

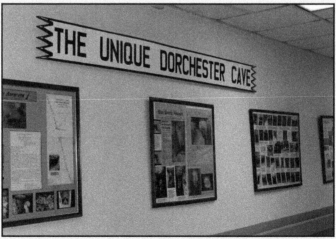

Dorchester Cave—and display—are located in basement of Sturgeon Bay Health Services

(Continued on following page)

DORCHESTER CAVE DISPLAY
(continued)

The third longest of Door County's caves, Dorchester is the only one formed along faults or joints in the dolostone of the Niagara Escarpment. The almost straight passage features offset walls and a flat ceiling. Most of an estimated forty caves in Door County are littoral caves, and two—Horseshoe Bay and Paradise Pit Caves—formed when rivers carved them from the bedrock.

For many years, Dorchester Cave lay hidden only six and a half feet beneath the hospital. Today it lies beneath the Sturgeon Bay Health Services' dining room. Makes you wonder what else might be lurking just beneath your feet.

Sturgeon Bay Health Services is located at 200 N 7th Ave, Sturgeon Bay, WI 54235. Website: http://www.sturgeonbayhs.com.

NEVILLE PUBLIC MUSEUM
BROWN COUNTY

The Neville dates to 1915 and the formation of the Green Bay Public Museum within the local library, with a goal of bringing art, history, and science to the region. When the museum outgrew expanded space in the library, George Mason and his wife donated funds to build a new museum, named after Mrs. Mason's parents, the Nevilles, as a memorial to their "work towards civic betterment in Green Bay," according to the museum's website.

A longtime permanent exhibit, On the Edge of the Inland Sea, presents thousands of artifacts, film footage, and photos documenting the history of Northeast Wisconsin from the end of the last Ice Age. The exhibit entrance is through a replica of a melting glacier. Beyond the glacier, exhibits portray the geology and ecology of the region, along with Native American life, early European settlements, and the development of lumbering, farming, and industry.

Visitors walk through a melting glacier to explore the geology of Northeast Wisconsin (Photo courtesy of the Neville Public Museum of Brown County)

Two other permanent exhibits sport a Packers theme, including the kid-friendly Discovery Room, which features a model of Lambeau Field constructed from thousands of Lego bricks by Milwaukee School of Engineering students. Recent temporary exhibits have examined the age of the dinosaurs, neon advertising signage, and celebrated Northeast Wisconsin's diverse cultures and traditions that have emigrated from across Latin America.

Recognized for its innovative programming, the Neville offers virtual exhibits, a virtual tour, and photos on its website. A long roster of enticing events—for example, Explorer Wednesdays (for kids), an astronomical society, dinner programs, and an international film festival—film the museum calendar with educational and entertaining programming.

Outdoors, a number of public sculptures grace the grounds and the trailhead for the self-guided Packers Heritage Trail begins at the Neville's front entrance. The trail features twenty-two commemorative bronze plaques, pointing out such sites as Curly Lambeau's childhood home, the birthplace of the Packers, the church where Vince Lombardi attended daily mass, and City Stadium, where the Packers played home games from 1925 to 1956.

Directions:	From the North, take U.S. Hwy. 41 south to Exit 171 and follow I-43 south. Take the Atkinson Dr. South Exit 189. Turn Right on Atkinson Drive and then the third exit at the roundabout to U.S. Hwy. 141 S/Velp Ave. Continue on Velp Avenue. Until Ashland Avenue. Turn right on Ashland Avenue. Continue to Dousman Street. In five blocks, turn right on Museum Place and then left into the parking lot. From the South (Milwaukee), take I-43 north to Exit 180 toward Austin Straubel Airport. Take the CR-X Exit to Riverside Drive. Turn right at Riverside and then left at Walnut Street. Turn right at Museum Place. From the South (Appleton), take U.S. Hwy. 41 north to Hwy. 41 Business Exit 163B to Ashland Avenue. Continue on Ashland to Walnut Street. Turn right at Walnut and then left at Museum Place.
Seasons/ Hours:	The museum is open from noon to 5 p.m. on Sunday; from noon to 8 p.m. on Tuesday; and from 9 a.m. to 5 p.m., Wednesday through Saturday. Closed on Mondays and holidays. Fee.
Amenities:	Gift shop, vending machines. Several parks and many dining opportunities can be found within a short distance of the museum.
Contact:	Neville Public Museum, 210 Museum Place, Green Bay, WI 54303-2760. Phone: 920/448-4460. Website: http://www.nevillepublicmuseum.org.

WISCONSIN HISTORICAL MUSEUM
DANE COUNTY

Tucked into a corner of the State Historical Museum's third floor, you can find a replica lead mine, complete with stick-in-tommies to light the dim interior and displays of early tools, minerals, and other mining-related artifacts. If the weather is inclement or you lack the time to visit one of Wisconsin's mine attractions, this replica is a good place to pick up some basic knowledge about the state's lead and zinc mining history. It also provides insight into both the difficulty and the importance of the Wisconsin's early mining efforts. The replica is part of the museum's permanent exhibit, On Common Ground: Two Hundred Years of Wisconsin History. The exhibit features displays relating to frontier life, the immigrant experience, and making a living in the early years of Wisconsin's history.

On the second floor you can find another permanent exhibit, People of the Woodlands: Wisconsin Indian Ways; changing exhibits are located on the first and fourth floors. The museum also contains a gift shop on the main floor offering books, cards, early toys, crafts, and other souvenirs.

The Wisconsin Historical Society also operates Pendarvis Historic Site, containing the restored buildings of a Cornish mining community in Mineral Point. (See Merry Christmas Mine, page 112)

Entrance to replica lead mine

Directions:	Located on the Capitol Square in downtown Madison at the intersection of Carroll and Mifflin Streets.
Seasons/ Hours:	Open 9 a.m. to 4 p.m., Tuesday through Saturday; closed on Sundays and major holidays. Donation requested.
Length:	You could easily spend a half day touring the museum. The length of the mine replica is about fifteen feet.
Amenities:	While you are on the Capitol Square, you also may want to visit the State Capitol and the Wisconsin Veterans Museum, located nearby on Mifflin Street. You can find a variety of restaurants and shops around the square and on State Street, which leads to the University of Wisconsin-Madison campus.
Contact:	Wisconsin Historical Museum, 30 N. Carroll St., Madison, WI 53703. Phone: 608/264-6555. Website: https://historicalmuseum.wisconsinhistory.org/.

SWINDLERS' RIDGE MUSEUM
LAFAYETTE COUNTY

Benton's small Swindler's Ridge Museum is worth a visit on a summer weekend, to view its exhibits related to all aspects of the local community, especially lead and zinc mining industry artifacts. The museum takes its name from a nearby ridge where miners once robbed lead from each others' diggings.

Directions:	Swindlers' Ridge Museum is located at 25 W. Main St., Benton. Main Street is also State Hwy. 11.
Seasons/ Hours:	Open from Memorial Day to Labor Day, 11 a.m. to 3 p.m., Saturday, Sunday, and Monday.
Contact:	Website: www.bentonwi.us/wp/?page_id=3.

UNIVERSITY OF WISCONSIN-MADISON GEOLOGY MUSEUM
DANE COUNTY

Combining visits to Wisconsin's underground sites with a trip to the Geology Museum can help put what you've seen outdoors into perspective and answer any lingering questions. The museum contains a lead-mining exhibit and samples of many different minerals found in the state, from common to rare forms. Fluorescent rocks are on display in their own black-lit room, and you won't want to miss (actually you can't) two large chunks of copper that were dragged deep into Wisconsin by glaciers. The biggest of these glacial erratics weighs more than a thousand pounds.

Fossils take up a large amount of the museum's space, including those of vertebrates, invertebrates, and plants. Considering that the largest fossil is the thirty-three-foot skeleton of a duck-billed dinosaur, perhaps it's no surprise that fossils compose the majority of the museum's square footage. Of course, some fossils are very small; you could hold a dozen tiny brachiopods in the palm of your hand. One case showcases Wisconsin's State Fossil: The trilobite lived during the Paleozoic Era, and went extinct 250 million years ago. Its flexible body enabled it to curl up in a ball when threatened.

The museum's cave replica also contains fossils, along with stalactites, stalagmites, flowstone, and other formations. The replica is a solution cave, hollowed out when acidic groundwater dissolved limestone or dolomite—a magnesium-rich limestone that often contains fossils. Cave development began beneath the water table as the acid water moved through cracks or joints in the bedrock. Eventually the water table lowered, and a stream flowed through the cave, cutting hollows into the walls and floor. Groundwater carrying dissolved limestone also seeped into the air-filled cave. Carbon dioxide was released and the mineral calcite deposited, creating the various formations.

You can learn more about the cave and other exhibits from a self-guided tour booklet available at the entrance—or download it from the website. Besides an overview of the exhibits, the booklet suggests activities for kids (or adults!) to try at home.

Directions:	Located at 1215 W. Dayton St., two blocks east of Camp Randall Stadium, on the University of Wisconsin-Madison campus.
Seasons/ Hours:	Monday through Friday, 8:30 a.m. to 4:30 p.m.; Saturday, 9 a.m. to 1 p.m. Closed on major holidays. Free.
Length:	The small, curved cave replica is approximately ten feet long.
Amenities:	Geology Museum is one block from Union South. The UW campus and Monroe Street areas offer many opportunities for shopping and dining.
Contact:	Geology Museum, Department of Geoscience, University of Wisconsin, 1215 W. Dayton St., Madison, WI 53706. Phone: 608/262-1412. Website: http://geoscience.wisc.edu/museum/.

PASSAGE THRU TIME MUSEUM

When you visit the restored Potosi Brewery and the National Brewery Museum (page 155), you may want to add a stop at the Passage Thru Time Museum, located on North Main Street, just blocks from the brewery. Its displays on local brewing, mining, and life along the Mississippi River can deepen your experience of the town's rich heritage. The museum also showcases arrowheads and other Native American artifacts, World War II memorabilia, and area agricultural history. An extensive collection of photos and historic records will interest family history buffs whose ancestors once lived in the region.

The museum is open from approximately May 15 to September 15, from noon to 4 p.m., Tuesday through Saturday. See: http://potosiwisconsin.com/passage-thru-time-museum/.

WEIS EARTH SCIENCE MUSEUM
WINNEBAGO COUNTY

Wisconsin's official mineralogical museum, the Weis Earth Science Museum belies the frequent stereotype of museums as stuffy collections of dusty stuff—though it contains plenty of unimaginably old specimens. Take the kids (and yourself) to the Weis to walk through a replica lead mine, create a dynamite blast in a quarry, and cause an earthquake. The interactive museum offers in-depth (pun intended) experiential education on Wisconsin's underground elements.

The Weis offers the usual background on Wisconsin's early lead mines, but the museum's real strength is in describing the state's heritage of iron and copper mining, along with Native American mining of materials for tools. Maps highlight areas where iron, copper, zinc, pipestone, and other deposits have been found or mined. Exhibits provide overviews of the Jackson County and Montreal iron mines, the Flambeau copper and gold mine, and the now-retracted Crandon copper and zinc mine. The museum also explains the state's use of lime and a variety of stone used in construction of private and public buildings.

Replica lead mine features a stick-in tommy.

Additional permanent exhibits examine plate tectonics, earthquakes, cloud formation, quarrying processes, and more earth-related research. The Dinosaur Den features a life-size skull replica of a Tyrannosaurus Rex, a complete Psittacosaurus with stones in its gizzard, a nest of dinosaur eggs, and a thigh bone of a duck-bill dinosaur that you can touch. The temporary exhibits currently include a history of the Montreal Mine and a description of the Niagara Escarpment in Wisconsin.

The museum's website offers downloadable publications on the escarpment, mining and other topics, as well as information on special events. Its Weis'n'Miners Geology Club serves people of all ages fascinated by minerals, fossils, lapidary and jewelry-making, geology, archaeology, gems, metaphysics, and mining. Organized in 2007, the club has grown into the largest geology club in Wisconsin!

Directions:	From the north take U.S. Hwy. 41 to the Oneida St. exit. Follow Oneida south to Midway Road, turn right (west) and proceed to the museum. From the south, take Hwy. 41 to the Hwy. 441/10 exit. Proceed to the Midway Rd. exit, turn right (east) and drive to the museum. From the east, take U.S. Hwy. 10 to Oneida St., turn right (north). Follow Oneida to Midway Road, turn left (west) and drive to the museum. From the west, take Hwy. 10 to the Midway Rd. exit, turn right (east) on Midway and proceed to the museum.
Seasons/ Hours:	Open from noon to 3 p.m., Monday through Friday; 10 a.m. to 5 p.m. on Saturday; and 1 p.m. to 5 p.m. on Sunday. Closed on holidays. Fee.
Length:	Lead mine tunnel is approximately fifteen feet long.
Amenities:	Adjacent to Barlow Planetarium on the University of Wisconsin-Fox Valley campus. Dining, shopping, and hotels available in Menasha.
Contact:	Weis Earth Science Museum, 1478 Midway Rd, Menasha, WI 54952. Information line: 920/832.2925. Website: http://www.weismuseum.org.

MATHIAS HAM HOUSE
DUBUQUE COUNTY, IOWA

Not surprisingly, underground sites are not always obvious. A tour of the 1856 Mathias Ham House—resembling an Italian villa filled with elegant antebellum European and American furnishings—includes a tour of its grounds, which showcase structures reflecting very different lifestyles.

The hillside features a replica lead mine, badger hut, and log cabin, pointing toward Ham's early success in lead mining. The oldest in Iowa, the 1833 log cabin was moved to this site to portray the home of an early mining family. It contains two rooms,

Inside the "lead mine"

one a bedroom and the other for daily activities, separated by a covered breezeway. The square badger hut is dug down into the earth, while the replica lead mine is dug into the side of the hill. It features a dirt floor, early mining artifacts, and a windlass at the top. An authentic one-room schoolhouse also stands on the grounds.

Owned and operated by the Dubuque County Historical Society, the Mathias Ham House is listed on the National Register of Historic Places. Costumed interpreters guide visitors through the house over the hillside.

Directions:	From U.S. Hwy. 151, take exit 60 toward Greyhound Park. Stay straight to go onto E. 16th Street. exit, and then turn right onto Kerper Boulevard. Turn left onto Fengler Street and then turn right onto Rhomberg Avenue. Turn left onto Shiras Avenue. Finally, turn right onto Lincoln Avenue.
Seasons/ Hours:	Open from Memorial Day through Labor Day, Wednesday through Sunday, from 11 a.m. to 4 p.m. Last tour leaves at 4 p.m. Fee—discounted when purchased with ticket to National Mississippi River Museum and Aquarium.
Amenities:	The National Mississippi River Museum and Aquarium (https://www.rivermuseum.com) offers a 4D theater, life on the Mississippi-related exhibits, stingray and paddlefish feeding times, and from spring to December tours of the *William R. Black* steam-propelled sidewheel dredge, a National Historic Landmark.
Contact:	Mathias Ham House, 2241 Lincoln Ave., Dubuque, IA 52001. Phone: 563/557-9545. Website: www.rivermuseum.com/hamhouse.

UNIVERSITY OF NORTHERN IOWA MUSEUM
BLACK HAWK COUNTY

Looking for a geological resource in Iowa? The University of Northern Iowa Museum in Cedar Falls began its natural history collections in 1892 and contains thousands of educational and research objects including minerals, rocks, and fossils. Now located in the Rod Library, the museum features history, anthropology, biology and other collections in addition to mineralogy, petrology, and paleontology.

Visit the website to learn about current exhibits. The website also provides access to a database of objects, including rocks and minerals; however, at this writing, no photos are available.

Directions:	To reach the museum, drive west from Dubuque roughly ninety miles to Cedar Falls on U.S. 20. Address: 1227 W 27th St, Cedar Falls, IA 50614.
Seasons/ Hours:	During the spring and fall semesters, the exhibit hall is open from 7 a.m. to midnight, Monday through Thursday; 7 a.m. to 7 p.m. on Friday; 10 a.m. to 5 p.m. on Saturday; and noon to midnight on Sunday. During summer session, hours are 7 a.m. to 8 p.m., Monday through Thursday; 7 a.m. to 5 p.m., on Friday; and noon to 5 p.m. on Sunday.
Amenities:	Cedar Falls boasts a performing arts center, sports dome, downtown shopping district, and various hotels and restaurants.
Contact:	To learn more, call 319/273-2838 or visit https://museum.library.uni.edu/.

A.E. SEAMAN MINERAL MUSEUM
HOUGHTON COUNTY, MICHIGAN

Designated the "Mineralogical Museum of Michigan" by the Michigan State Legislature in 1990, the A. E. Seaman Mineral Museum in Houghton, Michigan, features the largest public exhibit of specimens from the Great Lakes region. This impressive collection began in 1888, when the Michigan Mining School (now Michigan Technological University) began a systematic reference collection for its students. Officially founded in 1902, the A. E. Seaman Mineral Museum was named for its first curator in 1932.

At any one time, the Thomas D. Shaffner Exhibit Hall showcases about 4,000 specimens in several galleries organized around five educational themes— minerals as natural masterpieces, minerals of the Great Lakes region, minerals of the world, processes that form minerals, and minerals and society. Galleries supporting the minerals of the Great Lakes theme include those focused on Michigan copper and Lake Superior iron. One permanent exhibit that relates to the minerals and society theme educates about minerals used in automobile production.

Not far from the museum, the Copper Pavilion shelters the Guinness world record-holding chunk of lake copper. The seventeen-ton chunk was recovered from Lake Superior at Great Sand Bay along the Keweenaw Peninsula.

Directions:	From US 41 at the stoplight take MacInnes Drive uphill 1.1 miles and follow signage to the museum.
Seasons/ Hours:	Hours vary with academic schedule; generally open from Monday or Tuesday through Saturday. See website for specific times. Fee.
Amenities:	Handicap accessible. One onsite wheelchair available for visitors. Houghton offers several hotel, dining, and shopping opportunities.
Contact:	A. E. Seaman Mineral Museum, 1404 E. Ave., Houghton, MI 49931. Phone: 906/487-2572. Website: www.geo.mtu.edu/museum.

CLIFFS SHAFT MINE MUSEUM
MARQUETTE COUNTY, MICHIGAN

Cliffs Shaft Mine Museum does not offer tours deep underground, yet visitors can walk the tunnels the miners used to reach the base of the shaft. And there is much to see aboveground at the former iron mine site.

The mine operated almost continuously from 1879 to 1967, creating sixty-five miles of tunnels that reached a depth of 1358 feet. From 1887 until its closure, the mine produced more than twenty-six million tons of hematite.

Visitors first notice the obelisk-style headframes dating back to 1919 and the Koep hoist, the first used in the western hemisphere. The complex comprises several buildings in addition to the museum, which displays an assortment of headgear and other safety equipment, blasting and diamond drilling tools, rocks and minerals, and other artifacts. Visitors can see the blacksmith shop, iron ore cars, and, outdoors, a twelve-foot high iron ore truck weighing 170 tons. Standing in its thirty-ton shovel bucket is a popular photo opportunity.

Directions:	From U.S. Hwy. 41, turn southeast on Lakeshore Drive and then right onto Euclid Street
Seasons/ Hours:	From June through September, the museum is open 10 a.m. to 4 p.m., Tuesday through Saturday. Fee.
Amenities:	Ishpeming offers various dining and hotel options, along with shopping—for instance, you may want to check out Da Yoopers Tourist Trap: http:// dayoopers.com.
Contact:	Cliffs Shaft Mine Museum, 501 W Euclid St., Ishpeming, MI 49849. Phone: 906/485 -1882. Website: https://www.michigan.org/property/cliffs-shaft-mine-museum, or: https://www.facebook.com/cliffsshaft.

COPPERTOWN MINING MUSEUM

Despite its name, the Coppertown Mining Museum almost presents more community and cultural artifacts than mining objects. Still it's worth a visit and exhibits on minerals and prehistoric mining can be found along with recreations of a steam laundry, shoe shop, a pattern shop, a machine shop, and the C & H Hospital operating room.

Calumet grew as a company town alongside the Calumet and Heckla Mining Company, which produced more copper than any other Michigan mine. Besides the hospital and homes for workers, the company provided a theater and combination bathhouse and library. The Calumet and Heckla was known for both its generosity and paternalism toward employees.

Located in the mine's former pattern shop, the museum is one of almost two dozen heritage sites comprising the Keweenaw National Historical Park (https://www.nps.gov/kewe/index.htm), along with several of the other former mines listed here. A visit to Calumet just might entice you to make more trips to the rugged copper country of Upper Michigan.

Coppertown Mining Museum is open June through September, from 11 a.m. to 5 p.m., Monday through Saturday. Fee. It's located at 25815 Red Jacket Rd., Calumet, MI 49913.

CORNISH PUMPING ENGINE AND MINING MUSEUM
DICKINSON COUNTY, MICHIGAN

The largest steam-driven pumping engine ever built in the United States was constructed to dewater the Chapin Mine, since part of the iron ore body lay beneath a cedar swamp. Designed in 1890 by Edwin Reynolds of the E. P. Allis Company, Milwaukee (later Allis-Chalmers), the pump resembled those used by Cornish tin miners.

Originally housed in a massive sandstone pump house sixty feet high, the engine cracked as a result of several shifts in the earth and was dismantled in 1899. After the Oliver Mining Company acquired the Chapin Mine, it reassembled the pumping engine in 1907 and moved it to its current location near a Ludington Mine shaft. The Oliver Mining Company donated the engine to Dickinson County in 1934. The Menominee Range Historical Foundation took ownership of the pumping engine in 1978, and three years later it was listed on the National Register of Historic Places.

The pumping engine stands fifty-four feet and weighs 600 tons. In the Ludington Mine shaft, the pumping engine connected to a series of eight pumps, which carried water to the surface in eight steps. At its maximum speed, the pumping engine produced 1,200 horsepower and had a capacity of 3,400 gallons per minute.

In addition to the pumping engine, the museum showcases an admirable collection of Menominee Range iron mining equipment, for example, skips used to transport ore to the surface, man cars to transport miners to work areas, and a dynamite car. Several pieces of larger equipment are displayed on the museum grounds.

Directions:	Located on Kent Street, west of U.S. 2/141 in downtown Iron Mountain.
Seasons/Hours:	Open June 3 through Labor Day, from 9 a.m. to 5 p.m., Monday through Saturday. Fee.
Amenities:	Gift shop. Iron Mountain also offers the Menominee Range Historical Museum, a World War II Glider and Military History Museum, and the Millie Mine Bat Viewing Area (page 124).
Contact:	Cornish Pumping Engine and Mining Museum, 300 Kent St., Iron Mountain, MI 49801. Seasonal Phone: 906/774-1086. Website: www.menomineemuseum.com/cornish-pump.htm.

FINALLY...

Whether the project we contemplate means digging out glacial fill, exploring karst landscapes, surveying underground passages, studying bat populations, researching the impact of mining operations, or sharing our discoveries through tours or museum exhibitions, Wisconsin's underground environment promises a future rich with new knowledge. It will be interesting to see where our work takes us and where that mysterious environment leads.

End of the dig in Maribel New Hope Cave at
Cherney Maribel Caves County Park

Located on private land, this sinkhole could lead to an undiscovered cave.

ACKNOWLEDGMENTS

Once again, completing this second edition has provided both an adventure across and beneath Wisconsin, as well as a reminder of the wisdom and helpfulness of her citizens. Whatever I asked for, kindhearted people supplied—directions to new sites, photographs, or historical or geological information.

Counted first among those helpful folks is Kira Henschel, publisher at Henschel HAUS Publishing, Inc., who suggested this edition. Other contributors included Becky Rehl, communications and office manager at Folklore Village, Dodgeville; Ginny Haen, assistant curator, Door County Historical Museum and Archives, Sturgeon Bay; Kevin Swenson, park manager, Blue Mound State Park, Blue Mounds; Gayl Stewart, naturalist, Governor Dodge State Park, Dodgeville; Ruth Riesch, Earthaven Museum, Gillett; Joe Ferlo, president and CEO, Oshkosh Opera House Foundation, Oshkosh; Thomas Meyer, conservation biologist, State Natural Areas Program, Bureau of Natural Heritage Conservation, Wisconsin Department of Natural Resources; Connie Frazier, photographer, Boscobel; Colleen Tolliver, natural resource educator, Interstate State Park, Wisconsin Department of Natural Resources, St. Croix Falls; Kathy Vaillancourt, co-owner, Walker House, Mineral Point; Karen Braun, curator and assistant director, Racine Heritage Museum, Racine; Julie Coquard, vice president and marketing director, Wollersheim Winery and Distillery, Prairie du Sac; Lani Poynter, co-owner, Delaware Copper Mine, Mohawk, Michigan; Jennifer Redell, cave and mine specialist, Bureau of Natural Heritage Conservation, Wisconsin Department of Natural Resources, Madison; Matt Portfleet, co-owner, Adventure Mining Company, Greenland, Michigan; Jim Beloian, historian/guide; Dave Desimone, director, Black Point Estate, Lake Geneva; Tracey Lee Roberts, senior lecturer emerita, Department of History, University of Wisconsin-Platteville, Platteville; Holly Carlson, media and events coordinator, Sparta Chamber of Commerce, Sparta; Eric McMaster, co-owner, Crystal Cave, Spring Valley; Kelley Linehan, marketing and events manager, Bayfield Chamber and Visitor Bureau, Bayfield; Erik Flesch, museum director, and Mary Huck, education coordinator, The Mining and Rollo Jamison museums, Platteville; Jan Okeson, assistant manager, Cave of the Mounds-National Natural Landmark, Blue Mounds; Carol Abrahamzon, executive director, Mississippi Valley Conservancy, La

Crosse; Julie Rubel, owner, Crystal Lake Cave, L.L.C., Dubuque, Iowa; RJ & Linda Miller Photography, La Crosse; Patti Seidl, retail manager, Von Stiehl Winery, Algoma; Kevin Last, tour operations supervisor, Miller Brewing Company, Milwaukee; Vicki Schicker, curator, Jefferson Historical Museum, Jefferson; and many others (you know who you are!).

Besides Gary Soule, Wisconsin Speleological Society cave archivist and historian, who penned the Foreword and guided me around Door County caves, several other WSS members provided substantial expertise, including Kasey Fiske, chairman; Bryan Kleist, vice chairman; and Al Schema. Mary Lou Santovec provided several site leads and accompanied me on one adventure; and my husband Michael H. Knight joined me on others, in addition to providing encouragement and a divine listening ear when obstacles inevitably cropped up.

ABOUT THE AUTHOR

Doris Green follows her curiosity about education, genealogy, and the natural environment, creating articles for local, regional, and national publications. This topical diversity sometimes provides insights not found in more focused approaches.

This second edition of *Wisconsin Underground: A Guide to Caves, Mines, and Tunnels in and Around the Badger State* resulted from a conversation with the publisher of Green's fourth nonfiction book for general audiences, *Elsie's Story: Chasing a Family Mystery*. Both books trace their origin to a childhood trip to the Cave of the Mounds.

Green launched and co-published *Wisconsin Community Banker* magazine for the former Community Bankers of Wisconsin and was a communications specialist with the School of Human Ecology at the University of Wisconsin-Madison. She served as publisher at Magna Publications, also in Madison, which then had a higher education book division in addition to a national newsletter division.

She holds a bachelor's degree from the University of Wisconsin-Madison School of Education and a master's degree from the School of Journalism and Mass Communication. She lives with her husband, Michael H. Knight, and three distracting cats in a log house near Spring Green, Wisconsin.

Learn more and connect with the author at www.dorisgreenbooks.com.

Below Spring Cave entrance at Cherney Maribel Caves County Park
(Photo: Gary K. Soule)

CPSIA information can be obtained
at www.ICGtesting.com
Printed in the USA
BVHW090851300719
554634BV00005B/57/P